DATE DUE

30 July 86			
OCT 2 8 1987			
2/2/88			
11-14			
		WITHDRAWN	
GAYLORD			PRINTED IN U.S.A.

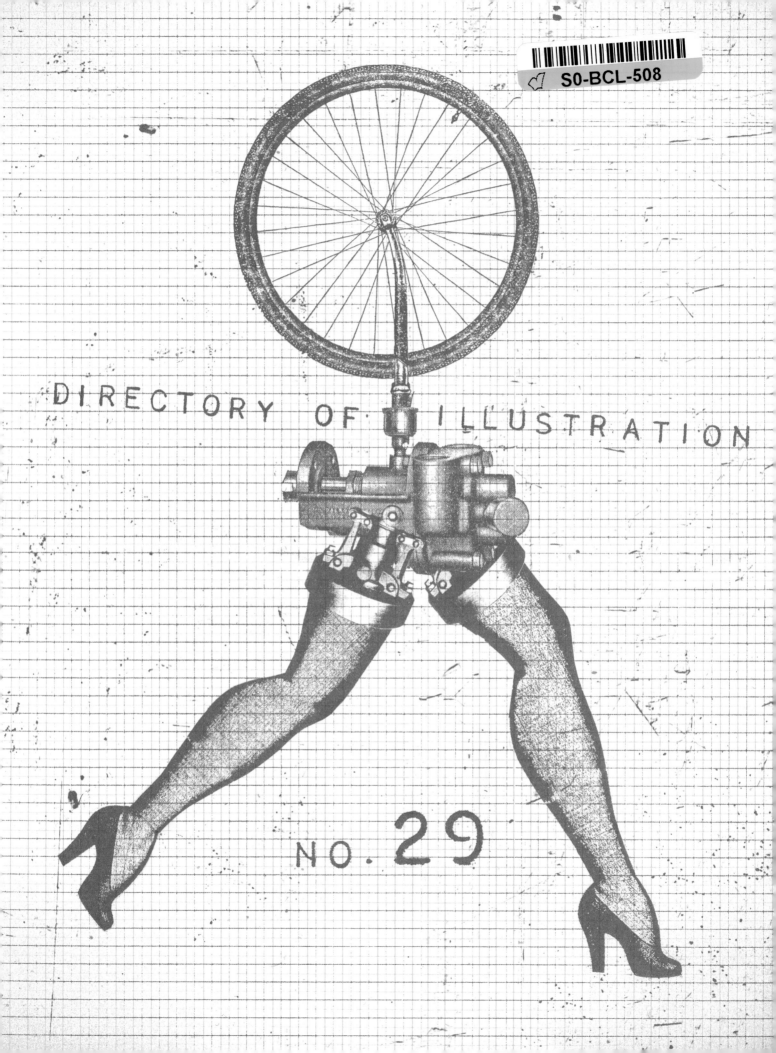

DIRECTORY OF ILLUSTRATION

NO. 29

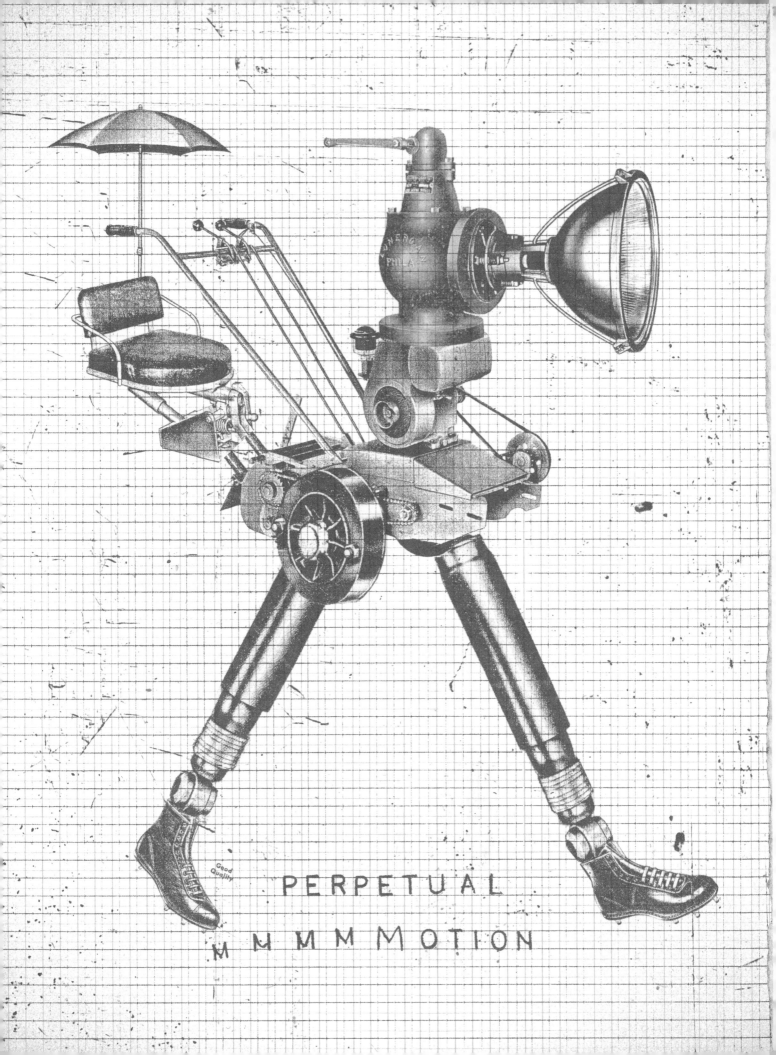

PERPETUAL

M M M M MOTION

no. 29

PERPETUAL MOTION

DIRECTORY OF ILLUSTRATION

PUBLISHER / EDITOR
Glen R. Serbin

**VICE PRESIDENT /
SOURCE BOOK DIRECTOR**
Elizabeth Nebb Owen

CONTROLLER
Mai Raack

MARKETING REPRESENTATIVES
Ellie Altomare
Adrian Johnson
Jo Ann Miller
Beth Pierson

DIRECTOR OF PRODUCTION
Tamra Dempsey

PRODUCTION MANAGER
Barbara Kuhn

PRODUCTION STAFF
Keane Roberts

PAGE DESIGN SERVICES
Theil Shelton

DISTRIBUTION COORDINATOR
Lynda Lou Moreno

PROOFING
Karen Bridgers
Julie Simpson

ACCOUNTING ASSISTANT
Johanna Wagner

**MANAGING EDITOR /
MAGAZINE DIVISION**
Julie Simpson

**MANAGER /
SITEDESIGNWORKS DIVISION**
Christina Henson

ADMINISTRATIVE SUPPORT
Kim Taylor

ACCOUNTING FIRM
Damitz, Brooks, Nightingale, Turner
& Morrisset

PRINTER
Toppan Printing Co., Ltd.

SHIPPING & MAILING
Express Logistics, Inc.

BOOK DESIGN & ART DIRECTION
Spur Design

COVER & INTERIOR ILLUSTRATIONS
David Plunkert
www.davidplunkert.com
see pages 358-359

PUBLISHED BY
Serbin Communications, Inc.
813 Reddick Street
Santa Barbara, California 93103
805-963-0439
www.serbin.com
email: info@serbin.com

A a

B b

C c

H h

I i

J j

K k

L l

● • ● ●

PETER BOLLINGER

shannonassociates.com

212.333.2551

SEAN RODWELL

ENVY

shannonassociates.com

212.333.2551

THE ONLY WAY TO GET IN IS TO WIN

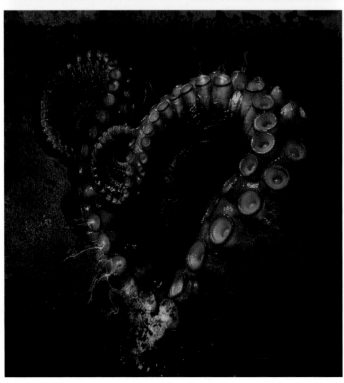

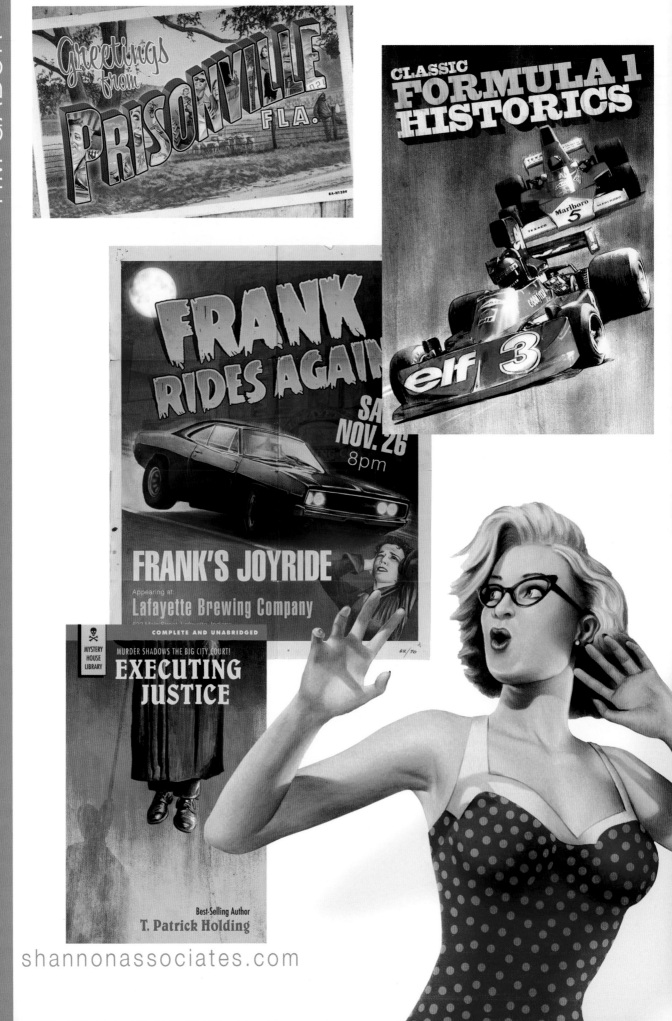

shannonassociates.com

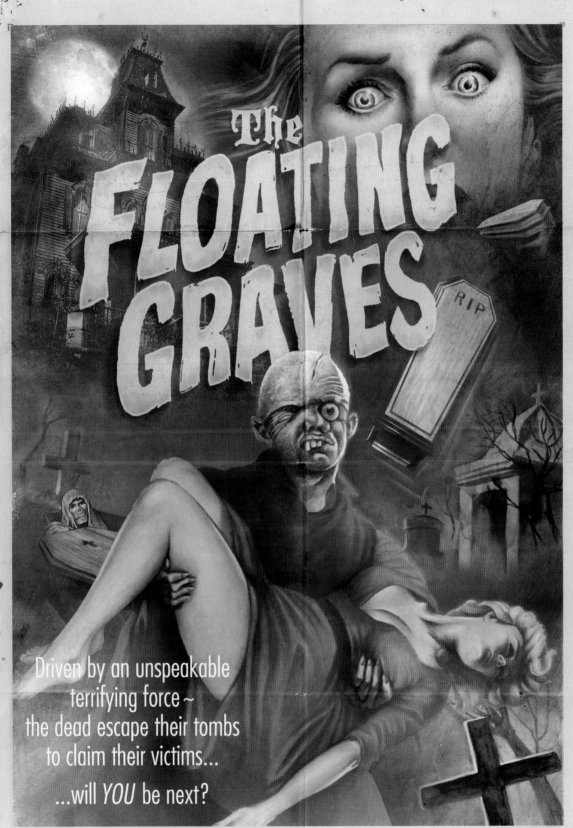

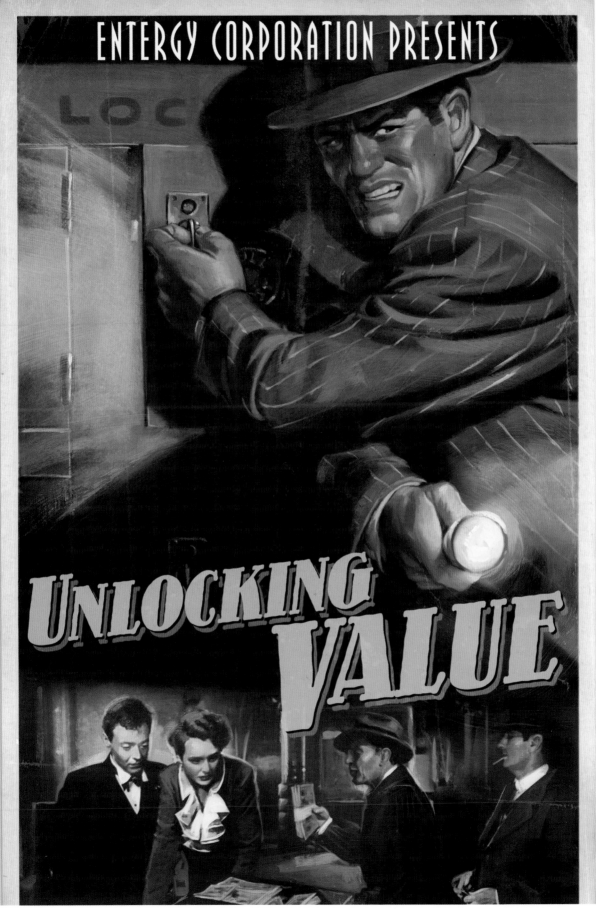

ENTERGY CORPORATION PRESENTS

UNLOCKING VALUE

MICHAEL KOELSCH

212.333.2551

shannonassociates.com

When I get up nothing gets me down.

Levi's for Life

212.333.2551

CHRISTOPHER PETERSON

TORSTEIN NORDSTRAND

shannonassociates.com

212.333.2551

MURILO MACIEL

212.333.2551

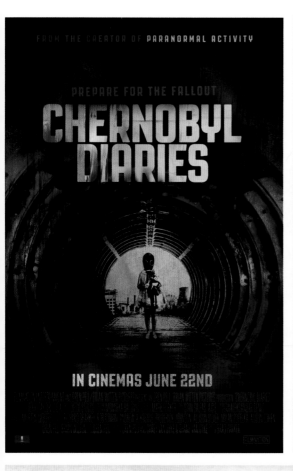

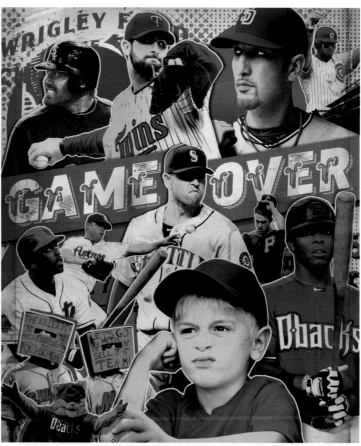

212.333.2551

BLAKE MORROW

JULIANA KOLESOVA

212.333.2551

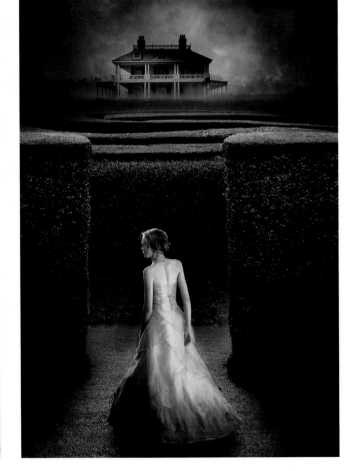

ANTONIO JAVIER CAPARO

212.333.2551

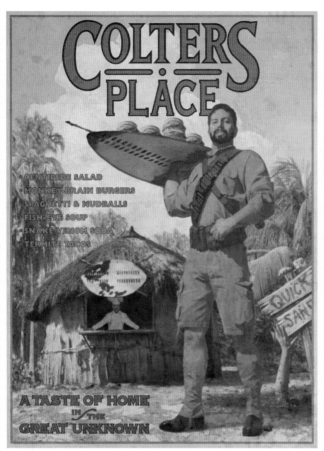

shannonassociates.com

SAM KENNEDY

212.333.2551

212.333.2551

shannonassociates.com

MARCH 15–21, 2012 | VOLUME 43 | NUMBER 11

PUBLIC MONEY PIT: ANDY THOMAS' DEATH-PENALTY-LADEN YEARS AS COUNTY ATTORNEY MADE DEFENSE ATTORNEYS RICH. **PAGE 10**

PHOENIXNEWTIMES.COM | FREE

PHOENIX
New Times

WRIGHT GOT IT WRONG

BY KATHLEEN VANESIAN

PATRICK FARICY

212.333.2551

ORIOL VIDAL

ERWIN HAYA

shannonassociates.com

JON PROCTOR

212.333.2551

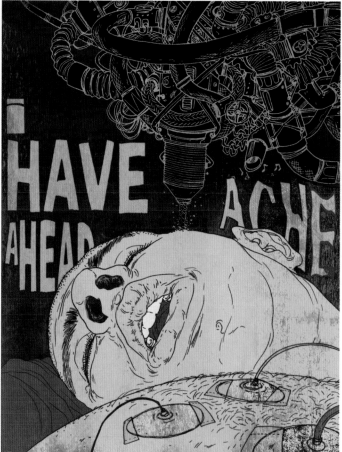

CRAIG PHILLIPS

212.333.2551

CRYSSY CHEUNG

shannonassociates.com

212.333.2551

MICHELLE LAMOREAUX

PASCAL CAMPION

shannonassociates.com

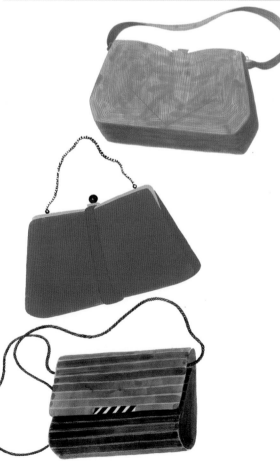

JENNIFER L. MEYER

ALI DOUGLASS

212.333.2551

Jeweled Fruit Salad

1/2 cup julienned peeled jicama

1/2 cup pomegranate seeds

2 medium ripe mangoes, peeled and thinly sliced

6 sliced, seeded kumquats

2 tablespoons fresh lime juice

2 blood oranges, peeled and sectioned

2 tangerines peeled and sectioned

2 tablespoons honey

1/8 teaspoon coarse sea salt

1/4 teaspoon ground red pepper

1 pear, thinly sliced

Combine all fruits in a large bowl and toss gently. Next combine the lime juice, honey, pepper, and salt in a small bowl, stirring well with a whisk. Pour dressing over fruit and toss gently to coat. Serve with your favorite champagne!

shannonassociates.com

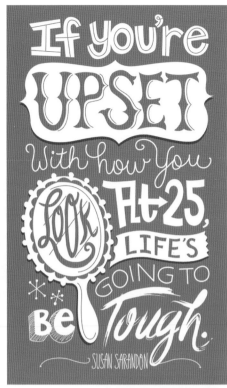

MONIKA ROE

212.333.2551

shannonassociates.com

Libby Boom

Octavius Hector
the Avid Collector

212.333.2551

shannonassociates.com

IKER AYESTARAN

SALLY WERN COMPORT

212.333.2551

shannonassociates.com

JULIANA NEUFELD

NEIL SWAAB

212.333.2551

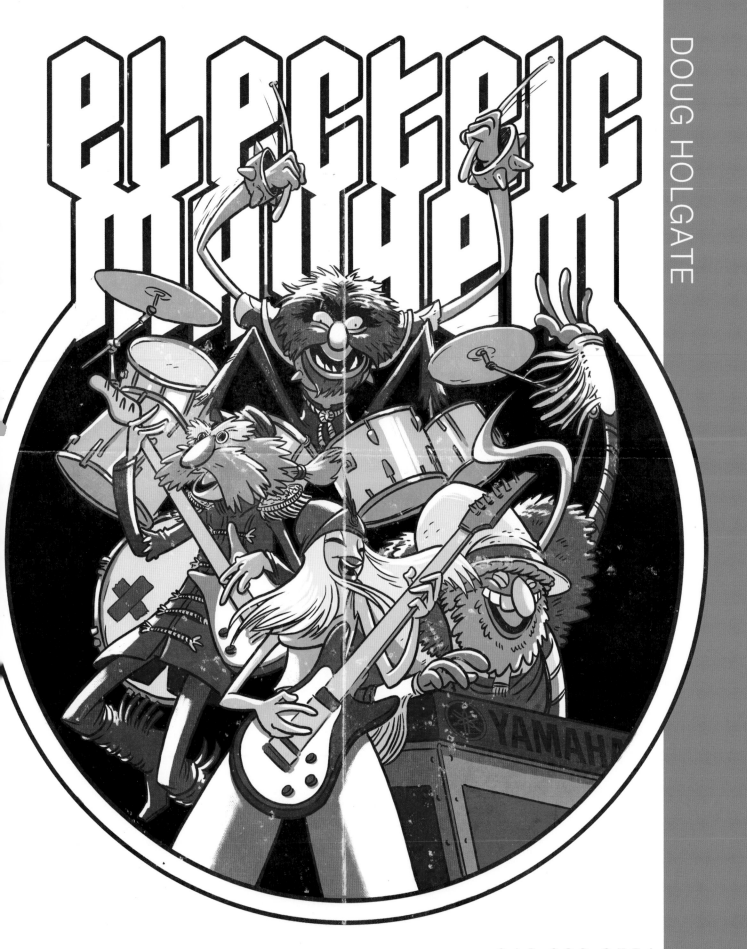

DOUG HOLGATE

212.333.2551

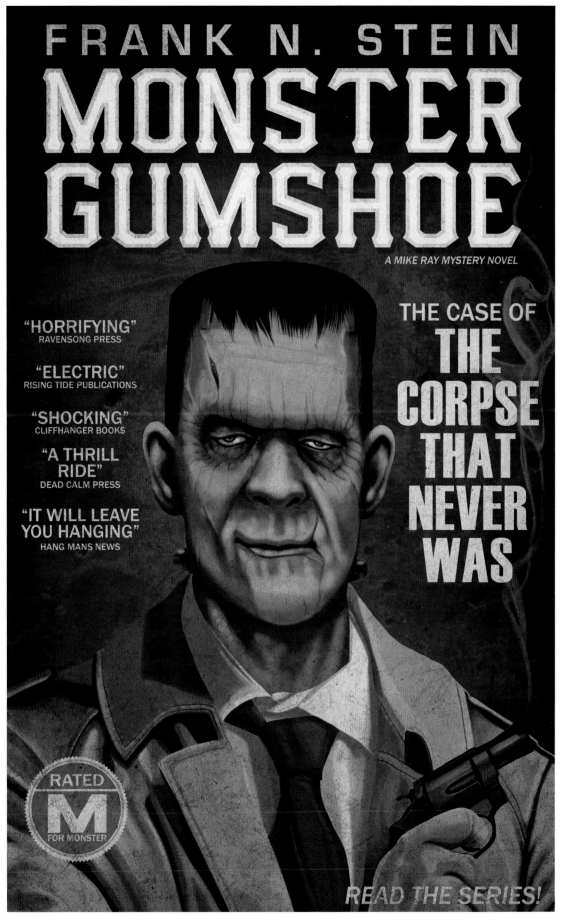

FRANK N. STEIN

MONSTER GUMSHOE

A MIKE RAY MYSTERY NOVEL

THE CASE OF
THE CORPSE THAT NEVER WAS

"HORRIFYING"
RAVENSONG PRESS

"ELECTRIC"
RISING TIDE PUBLICATIONS

"SHOCKING"
CLIFFHANGER BOOKS

"A THRILL RIDE"
DEAD CALM PRESS

"IT WILL LEAVE YOU HANGING"
HANG MANS NEWS

RATED
M
FOR MONSTER

READ THE SERIES!

212.333.2551

shannonassociates.com

212.333.2551

NOIRGALEY · MADRID

ANANKE

ERWIN MADRID

212.333.2551

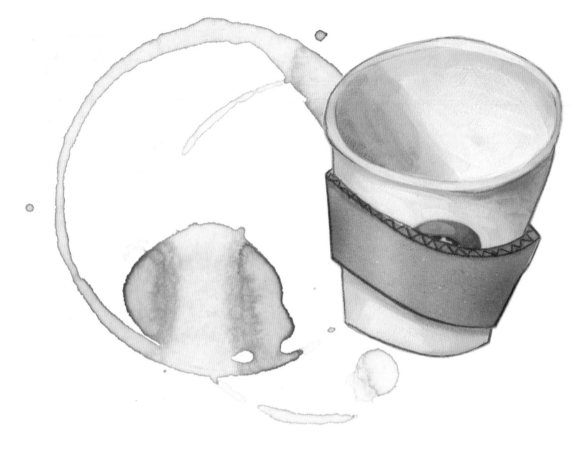

MARYN ROOS

JOHN SHROADES

212.333.2551

shannonassociates.com

RICHARD COWDREY

212.333.2551

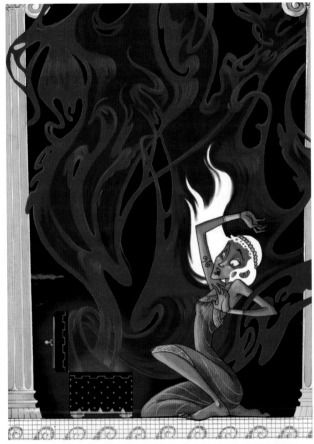

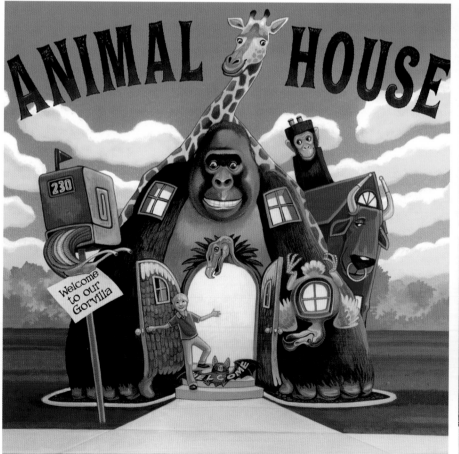

ENRIQUE CORTS

GERALD GUERLAIS

212.333.2551

HANSEN   ALEXANDERSEN   BARRETT   BELL

BENDALL-BRUNELLO   BLACKMORE   CALO   CASTELAO

CHAN   CIMATORIBUS   CURTIS   FRANCIS

HALEY   HALL   HENRY   HIBBERT

KOBER   LAUGESEN   LEICK   LOVERIDGE

LUXICH

MONESCILLO

O'KIF

OBERDIECK

ONG

PATTERSON

SIMON

STOJIC

VAUGHAN

WAKEFIELD

WOOD

ZENZ

KID

shannon

featuring over 150 premier children's book illustrators

BERNSTEIN & ANDRIULLI

www.ba-reps.com   *artinfo@ba-reps.com*   *212.6821490*

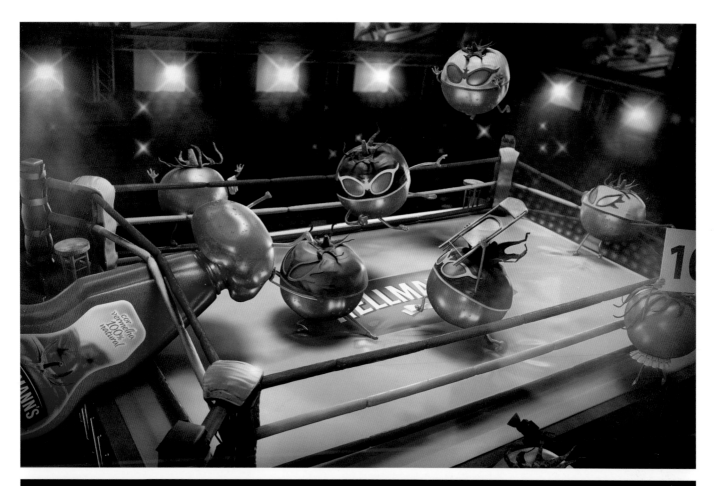

MMJ STUDIO

BERNSTEIN & ANDRIULLI

www.ba-reps.com   *artinfo@ba-reps.com*   *212.6821490*   81

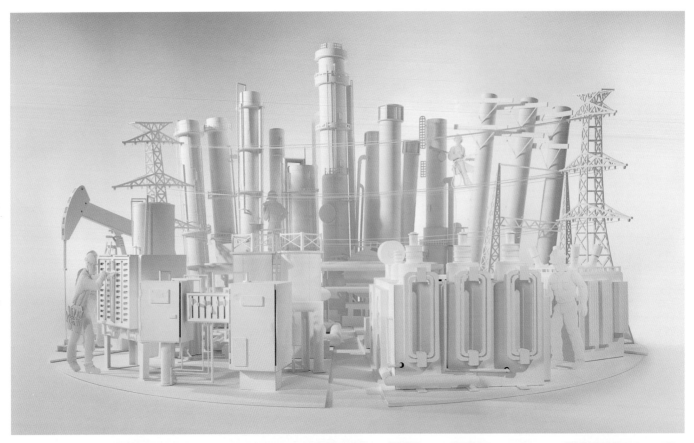

BERNSTEIN & ANDRIULLI

www.ba-reps.com   *artinfo@ba-reps.com*   *212.6821490*

SHOTOPOP

BERNSTEIN & ANDRIULLI

www.ba-reps.com   *artinfo@ba-reps.com*   *212.6821490*

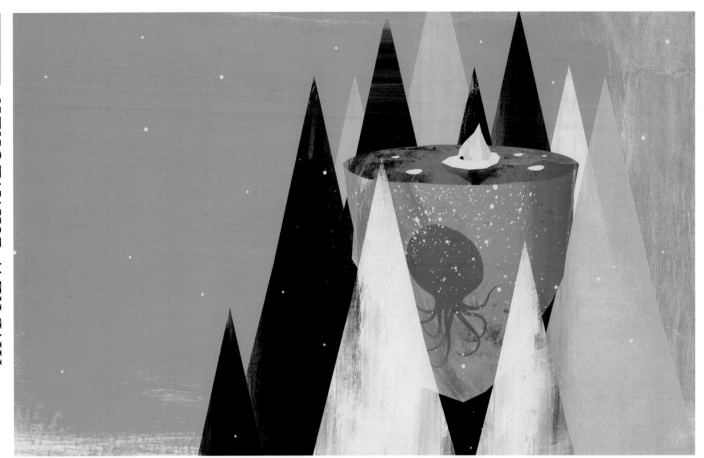

BERNSTEIN & ANDRIULLI

www.ba-reps.com   *artinfo@ba-reps.com*   *212.6821490*

OLAF HAJEK

BERNSTEIN & ANDRIULLI

www.ba-reps.com   artinfo@ba-reps.com   212.6821490   85

人見人愛

cute   Neiko Ng

BERNSTEIN & ANDRIULLI

www.ba-reps.com   artinfo@ba-reps.com   212.6821490

JOSIE PORTILLO

BERNSTEIN & ANDRIULLI

www.ba-reps.com   *artinfo@ba-reps.com*   *212.6821490*

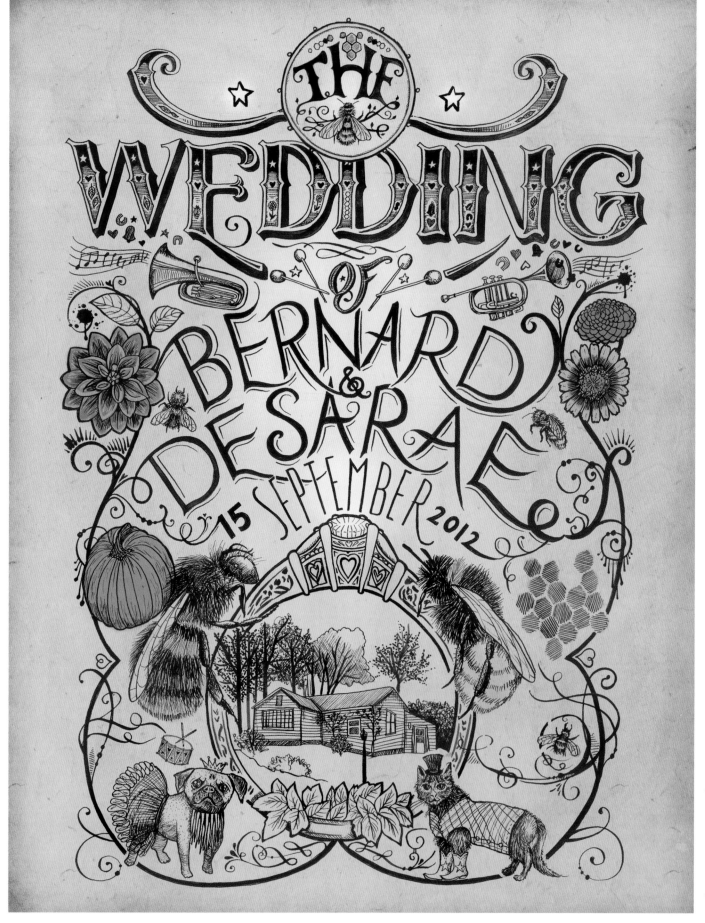

BERNSTEIN & ANDRIULLI

www.ba-reps.com   *artinfo@ba-reps.com*   *212.6821490*

EXPERIENCE ENHANCER DEVICE
XV YEARS LIVING KICK ASS EXPERIENCES

EXPERIENCE ENHANCER DEVICE
XV YEARS LIVING KICK ASS EXPERIENCES

ADOBE & *creativity*

VASAVA

BERNSTEIN & ANDRIULLI

www.ba-reps.com   artinfo@ba-reps.com   212.6821490

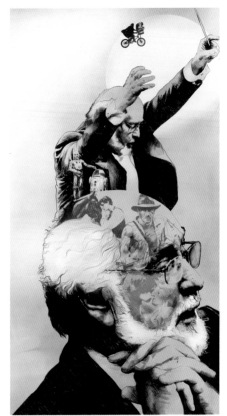

Comm. by The Wall Street Journal.　　Comm. for Acqua Colonia.

Comm. for Fiat.

Gabriel Moreno

début **art** • Illustrators, Photographers and Fine Artists Agents
30 Tottenham Street, London, W1T 4RJ. United Kingdom
Tel: 01144 20 7636 1064. Fax: 01144 20 7580 7017
The Coningsby Gallery • Tel: 01144 20 7636 7478

email: **info@debutart.com** • **www.debutart.com**

début **art**

début **art**

début **art** • Illustrators, Photographers and Fine Artists Agents
30 Tottenham Street, London, W1T 4RJ. United Kingdom
Tel: 01144 20 7636 1064. Fax: 01144 20 7580 7017
The Coningsby Gallery • Tel: 01144 20 7636 7478
email: **info@debutart.com** • **www.debutart.com**

the coningsby gallery

Since 1985, *début* **art** (based in London, England and now with offices in New York and Paris) has proactively sought out leading contemporary image-makers & clients who create original, progressive and commercially successful media material. Today, *début* **art** and the highly artistic illustrators it promotes, are widely regarded, both in the UK and around the world, as representing one of the finest and most contemporary talent groupings in the field of illustration.

début **art** and the illustrators it markets have successfully undertaken assignments worldwide for very many companies that are leaders in their fields including: Microsoft, Apple, Coca-Cola, Proctor and Gamble, Samsung, Levi's, Nokia, Rolls-Royce, BP, Shell, Nike, The Chicago Mercantile Exchange, The NYSE, The London Stock Exchange, Bloomberg, American Express, Barclaycard, HSBC, IBM, British Airways, Unilever, Harrods, Selfridges, Macy's (New York), McDonalds Topshop, Verizon, Lucas Inc, The Royal Opera House (London), Universal Music, Sony, Miller, Burton, Harper Collins, The Wall Street Journal, The New York Times, The Times (London), Le Monde, The Economist, The Financial Times, Vogue, Cosmopolitan and National Geographic Magazine.

Full portfolios for every artist can be reviewed and requested via our web site at **www.debutart.com**

The Coningsby Gallery stages some 30 exhibitions per year by selected leading illustrators, photographers and fine artists. Review of previous exhibitions, a look at upcoming shows and a photo tour of the gallery itself can be accessed at **www.coningsbygallery.com**

Contact: Andrew Coningsby, Samuel Summerskill, Jonathan Hedley and Rhiannon Lloyd

Alan Aldridge	Paul Davis	Drawn Ideas	Stephane Manel	Steve Rawlings	Dominic Trevett
Arno	Carol del Angel	ilovedust	Sophie Marsham	Nick Reddyhoff	Triggerfish 21
Andrew Baker	Pierre Doucin	Infomen	Kim McGillivray	The Red Dress	Alex Trochut
Istvan Banyai	Barry Downard	Jacey	Vince McIndoe	Redseal	Jim Tsinganos
Gary Bates	Katie Edwards	Jackdaw	Wesley Merritt	Cath Riley	Vault49
Jon Berkeley	El Señor	Sarah Jones	Justin Metz	Craig Robinson	Stephanie von Reiswitz
Chris Bianchi	Tim Ellis	Alan Kitching	Gabriel Moreno	Kerry Roper	Jeff Wack
Jacquie Boyd	Sam Falconer	Eley Kishimoto	Patrick Morgan	Saeko	Stephan Walter
Norm Breyfogle	Jo Fernihough	Viktor Koen	Morten Morland	Serge Seidlitz	Neil Webb
Jon Burgerman	Flatliner	Ronald Kurniawan	Huntley/Muir	Seripop	Jane Webster
Oliver Burston	Helen Friel	Christina K	Chris Nurse	Shape & Colour	Joe Wilson
Benedict Campbell	Peter Grundy	Yuko Kondo	Kevin O'Keefe	Craig Shuttlewood	Oscar Wilson
Danny Capozzi	Sarah Hanson	Kolchoz	Martin O'Neill	Niels Shoe Meulman	Alex Williamson
James Carey	Jethro Haynes	La Boca	Alex Pang	Michel Streich	Tina Zellmer
Celyn	Sarah Haywood	Chris Labrooy	Paper Work	Sroop Sunar	Jurgen Ziewe
Russell Cobb	Matt Herring	Yann Legendre	Mac Premo	Tado	Vasili Zorin
Matthew Cooper	Oliver Hibert	Neil Leslie	Pietari Posti	James Taylor	
Peter Crowther	Nanette Hoogslag	Lie-ins & Tigers	Chris Price	The Studio	
Marta Cerda	Sarah Howell	Andy Lovell	Paul Price	Yehrin Tong	
Matthew Dartford	Frazer Hudson	Harry Malt	Peter Quinnell	Sophie Toulouse	

'Beauty is truth, truth beauty'
John Keats

Self-initiated.

Comm. for L'Oréal.

Comm. by Dash Magazine.

Comm. by Alexander McQueen.

Patrick Morgan

début **art** • Illustrators, Photographers and Fine Artists Agents
30 Tottenham Street, London, W1T 4RJ. United Kingdom
Tel: 01144 20 7636 1064. Fax: 01144 20 7580 7017
The Coningsby Gallery • Tel: 01144 20 7636 7478

email: **info@debutart.com** • **www.debutart.com**

Comm. by Time Out New York.

Comm. by Boston Magazine.

Comm. by Blink Magazine.

Comm. for Vodafone.

Stephan Walter

début **art** • Illustrators, Photographers and Fine Artists Agents
30 Tottenham Street, London, W1T 4RJ. United Kingdom
Tel: 01144 20 7636 1064. Fax: 01144 20 7580 7017
The Coningsby Gallery • Tel: 01144 20 7636 7478

email: **info@debutart.com** • **www.debutart.com**

début **art**

Comm. by Hip Opsession.

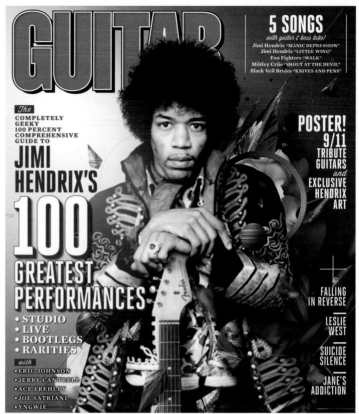

Comm. by Guitar World Magazine.

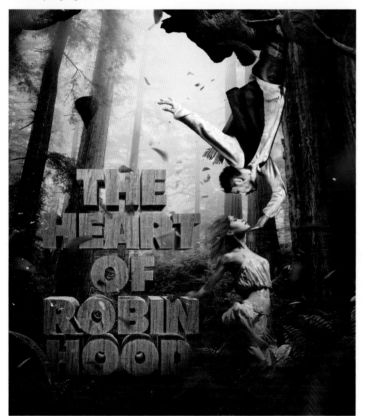

Comm. by The Royal Shakespeare Company.

Comm. for Sprite.

Pierre Doucin

début **art** • Illustrators, Photographers and Fine Artists Agents
30 Tottenham Street, London, W1T 4RJ. United Kingdom
Tel: 01144 20 7636 1064. Fax: 01144 20 7580 7017
The Coningsby Gallery • Tel: 01144 20 7636 7478

email: **info@debutart.com** • **www.debutart.com**

début **art**

Comm. by a world leading watchmaker.

Comm. by Harrods Magazine.

Comm. by Duke University Magazine.

Comm. for BP.

Alex Williamson

début **art** • Illustrators, Photographers and Fine Artists Agents
30 Tottenham Street, London, W1T 4RJ. United Kingdom
Tel: 01144 20 7636 1064. Fax: 01144 20 7580 7017
The Coningsby Gallery • Tel: 01144 20 7636 7478

email: **info@debutart.com** • **www.debutart.com**

début **art**

Comm. by Fortune Magazine.

SOUTHBANK CENTRE'S

WINTER
FESTIVAL

UNTIL 11 JANUARY 2012

ENJOY MAGICAL FAMILY SHOWS, BUSTLING CHRISTMAS MARKETS,
FREE EVENTS AND FESTIVE FOOD & DRINK

Comm. by The South Bank Centre (London).

Comm. by Toronto Life Magazine.

Comm. by Vanity Fair Magazine.

James Taylor

début **art** • Illustrators, Photographers and Fine Artists Agents
30 Tottenham Street, London, W1T 4RJ. United Kingdom
Tel: 01144 20 7636 1064. Fax: 01144 20 7580 7017
The Coningsby Gallery • Tel: 01144 20 7636 7478

email: **info@debutart.com** • **www.debutart.com**

début **art**

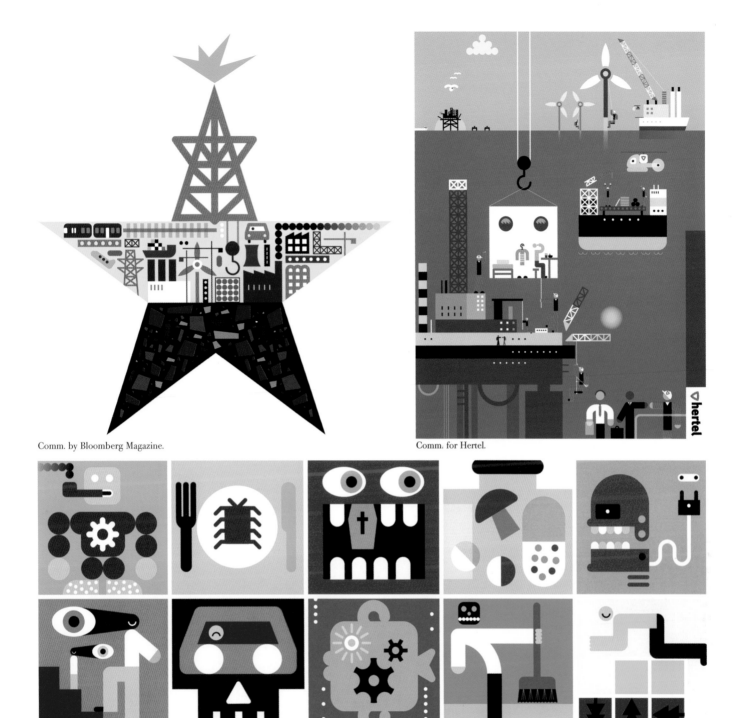

Comm. by Bloomberg Magazine.

Comm. for Hertel.

Comm. by Reader's Digest.

Peter Grundy

début **art** • Illustrators, Photographers and Fine Artists Agents
30 Tottenham Street, London, W1T 4RJ. United Kingdom
Tel: 01144 20 7636 1064. Fax: 01144 20 7580 7017
The Coningsby Gallery • Tel: 01144 20 7636 7478

email: **info@debutart.com** • **www.debutart.com**

Comm. for Banque Populaire.

Comm. for Darty.

Comm. by Fry & Torres.

Chris Labrooy

début **art** • Illustrators, Photographers and Fine Artists Agents
30 Tottenham Street, London, W1T 4RJ. United Kingdom
Tel: 01144 20 7636 1064. Fax: 01144 20 7580 7017
The Coningsby Gallery • Tel: 01144 20 7636 7478

email: **info@debutart.com** • **www.debutart.com**

Comm. by Scientific American Magazine.

Self-initiated.

Self-initiated.

début art

Comm. for Taco Bell.

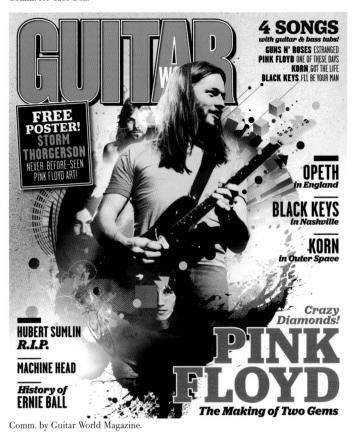

Comm. by Guitar World Magazine.

Comm. by Z-Life Magazine.

Jackdaw

début **art** • Illustrators, Photographers and Fine Artists Agents
30 Tottenham Street, London, W1T 4RJ. United Kingdom
Tel: 01144 20 7636 1064. Fax: 01144 20 7580 7017
The Coningsby Gallery • Tel: 01144 20 7636 7478

email: **info@debutart.com** • **www.debutart.com**

début art

Comm. by The Economist.

Comm. by BBC Focus Magazine.

Comm. by Fast Company Magazine.

Viktor Koen

début **art** • Illustrators, Photographers and Fine Artists Agents
30 Tottenham Street, London, W1T 4RJ. United Kingdom
Tel: 01144 20 7636 1064. Fax: 01144 20 7580 7017
The Coningsby Gallery • Tel: 01144 20 7636 7478

email: **info@debutart.com** • **www.debutart.com**

début **art**

Self-initiated.

Comm. by Real Deals Magazine.

Comm. by Men's Health Magazine.

Peter Crowther Associates

début **art** • Illustrators, Photographers and Fine Artists Agents
30 Tottenham Street, London, W1T 4RJ. United Kingdom
Tel: 01144 20 7636 1064. Fax: 01144 20 7580 7017
The Coningsby Gallery • Tel: 01144 20 7636 7478

email: **info@debutart.com** • **www.debutart.com**

Comm. by Sunday Times Travel Magazine.

Comm. by Men's Fitness Magazine.

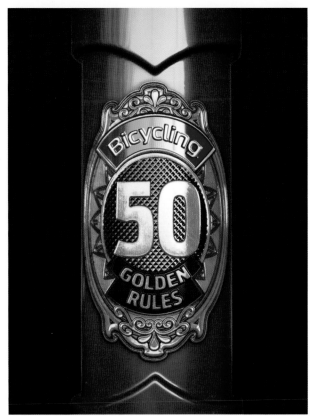

Comm. by Bicycling Magazine.

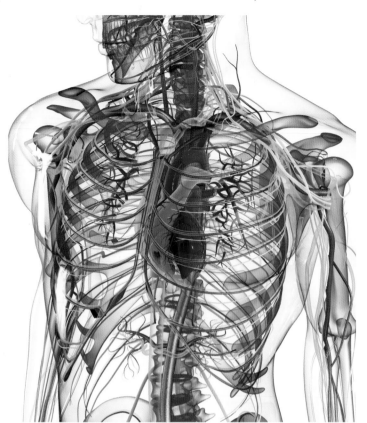

Comm. by Men's Health Magazine.

Comm. by Men's Fitness Magazine.

Comm. by GQ Magazine.

Peter Crowther Associates

début **art** • Illustrators, Photographers and Fine Artists Agents
30 Tottenham Street, London, W1T 4RJ. United Kingdom
Tel: 01144 20 7636 1064. Fax: 01144 20 7580 7017
The Coningsby Gallery • Tel: 01144 20 7636 7478

email: **info@debutart.com** • **www.debutart.com**

Comm. by Whole Living Magazine.

Comm. by Men's Fitness Magazine.

Comm. by Bicycling Magazine.

Comm. by F1 Magazine.

début **art**

Self-initiated.

Comm. by Global Trading Review Magazine.

Comm. by Esquire Magazine.

The Red Dress

début **art** • Illustrators, Photographers and Fine Artists Agents
30 Tottenham Street, London, W1T 4RJ. United Kingdom
Tel: 01144 20 7636 1064.   Fax: 01144 20 7580 7017
The Coningsby Gallery • Tel: 01144 20 7636 7478

email: **info@debutart.com** • **www.debutart.com**

Comm. by Popular Science Magazine.

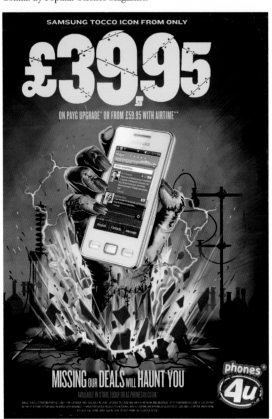

Comm. for Phones 4 U.

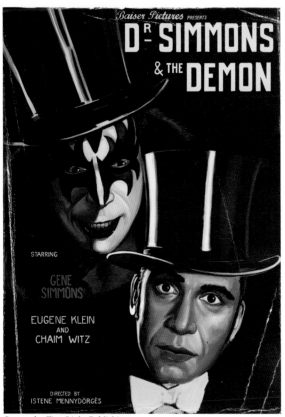

Comm. by First Light Publishing.

Comm. for Volvo's LIV Magazine.

'Miai Barbu'. Comm. for Discovery Channel.

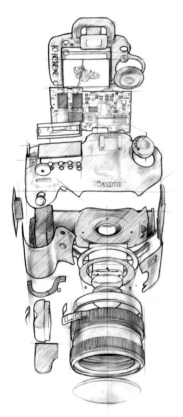

Comm. by Dorling Kindersley Publishing.

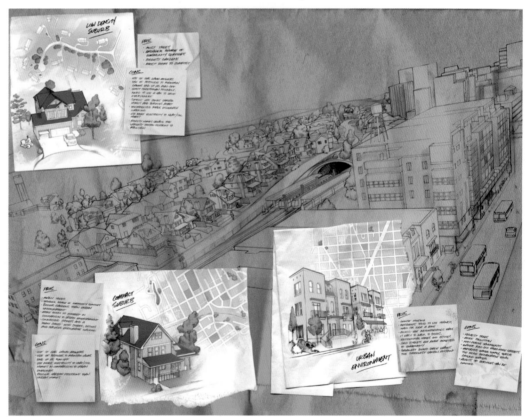

Comm. by The Franklin Institute.

James Carey

début **art** • Illustrators, Photographers and Fine Artists Agents
30 Tottenham Street, London, W1T 4RJ. United Kingdom
Tel: 01144 20 7636 1064. Fax: 01144 20 7580 7017
The Coningsby Gallery • Tel: 01144 20 7636 7478

email: **info@debutart.com** • **www.debutart.com**

'Gordon Ramsay'. Comm. by Apex Magazine.

Comm. by Experience Magazine.

Comm. for Mountain Dew.

Comm. by ESPN Magazine.

début art

Comm. for Stolichnaya Vodka.

Comm. by The Smithsonian Institute.

Comm. by Ted Baker Clothing.

Comm. by The Times

Vince McIndoe

début **art** • Illustrators, Photographers and Fine Artists Agents
30 Tottenham Street, London, W1T 4RJ. United Kingdom
Tel: 01144 20 7636 1064. Fax: 01144 20 7580 7017
The Coningsby Gallery • Tel: 01144 20 7636 7478

email: **info@debutart.com** • **www.debutart.com**

110

Comm. by McDonald's for Coca-Cola tie-in.

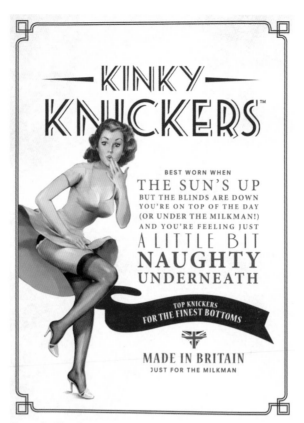

Comm. for Mary Portas.

Comm. for Anheuser Busch.

Comm. for The Ross Poster Group.

CARNIVAL OF THE COCKTAIL

Comm. for 42Below Vodka.

Self-initiated.

Comm. by Maharishi.

INFUSED

Comm. for Bombay Sapphire Gin.

Yehrin Tong

début **art** • Illustrators, Photographers and Fine Artists Agents
30 Tottenham Street, London, W1T 4RJ. United Kingdom
Tel: 01144 20 7636 1064. Fax: 01144 20 7580 7017
The Coningsby Gallery • Tel: 01144 20 7636 7478

email: **info@debutart.com** • **www.debutart.com**

début **art**

Chris Price. Self-initiated.

Chris Price. Comm. by Harpers Bazaar.

Sarah Hanson. Self-initiated.

Sarah Hanson. Comm. by New York Magazine.

début **art** • Illustrators, Photographers and Fine Artists Agents
30 Tottenham Street, London, W1T 4RJ. United Kingdom
Tel: 01144 20 7636 1064. Fax: 01144 20 7580 7017
The Coningsby Gallery • Tel: 01144 20 7636 7478

email: **info@debutart.com** • **www.debutart.com**

début **art**

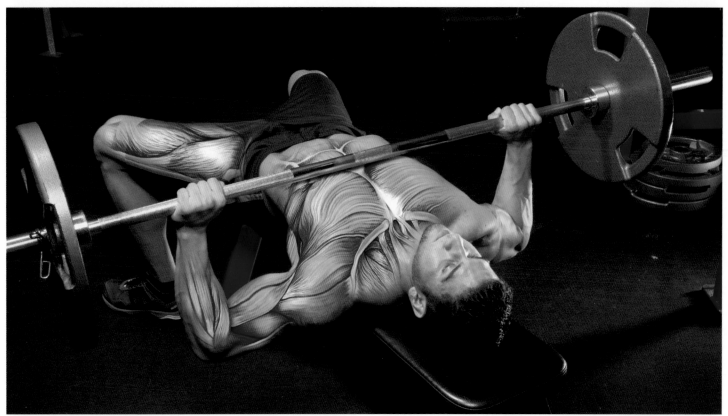

Comm. by Muscle and Fitness Magazine.

Comm. by The Banker Magazine.

Comm. by Inside Housing Magazine.

Oliver Burston

début **art** • Illustrators, Photographers and Fine Artists Agents
30 Tottenham Street, London, W1T 4RJ. United Kingdom
Tel: 01144 20 7636 1064. Fax: 01144 20 7580 7017
The Coningsby Gallery • Tel: 01144 20 7636 7478

email: **info@debutart.com** • **www.debutart.com**

début **art**

Comm. for Mzanzi TV Channel (South Africa).

Comm. for ABSA Bank.

Comm. for Stanley Tools.

Comm. for Pringles.

Barry Downard

début **art** • Illustrators, Photographers and Fine Artists Agents
30 Tottenham Street, London, W1T 4RJ. United Kingdom
Tel: 01144 20 7636 1064. Fax: 01144 20 7580 7017
The Coningsby Gallery • Tel: 01144 20 7636 7478

email: **info@debutart.com** • **www.debutart.com**

début **art**

Self-initiated.

Comm. by Atlanta Magazine.

Comm. by Fortune Magazine.

Serge Seidlitz

début **art** • Illustrators, Photographers and Fine Artists Agents
30 Tottenham Street, London, W1T 4RJ. United Kingdom
Tel: 01144 20 7636 1064. Fax: 01144 20 7580 7017
The Coningsby Gallery • Tel: 01144 20 7636 7478

email: **info@debutart.com** • **www.debutart.com**

Comm. by Educational Insights.

Self-initiated.

Comm. for Rover.

Comm. for Red Lobster Restaurants.

début **art**

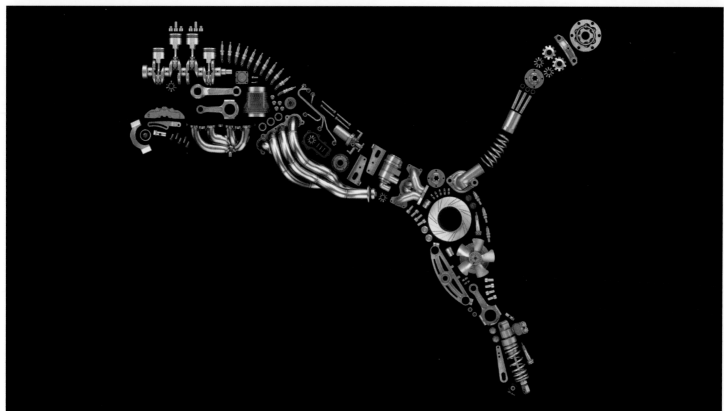

Comm. for Puma.

Comm. by Popular Science Magazine.

Matthew Dartford / Flip CG

début **art** • Illustrators, Photographers and Fine Artists Agents
30 Tottenham Street, London, W1T 4RJ. United Kingdom
Tel: 01144 20 7636 1064. Fax: 01144 20 7580 7017
The Coningsby Gallery • Tel: 01144 20 7636 7478

email: **info@debutart.com** • **www.debutart.com**

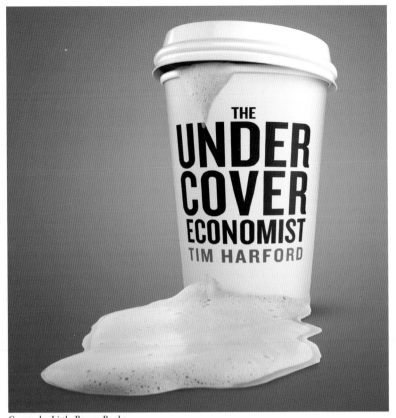
Comm. by Little Brown Books.

Comm. for Stella Artois.

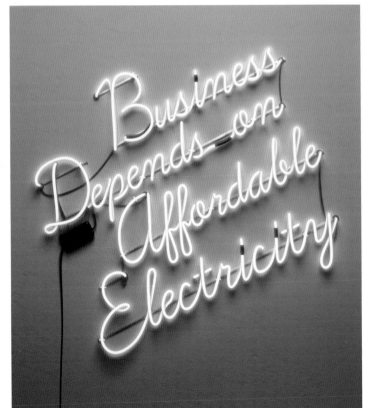
Comm. for Tristate.

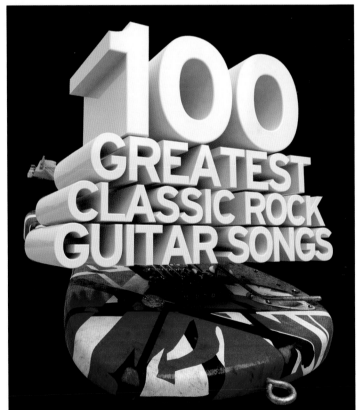
Comm. by Guitar World Magazine.

Comm. by Apex Magazine.

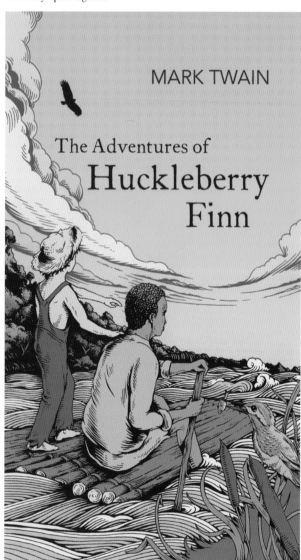

Comm. by Random House Publishing.

Comm. for Infiniti.

Joe Wilson

début **art** • Illustrators, Photographers and Fine Artists Agents
30 Tottenham Street, London, W1T 4RJ. United Kingdom
Tel: 01144 20 7636 1064. Fax: 01144 20 7580 7017
The Coningsby Gallery • Tel: 01144 20 7636 7478

email: **info@debutart.com** • **www.debutart.com**

Self-initiated.

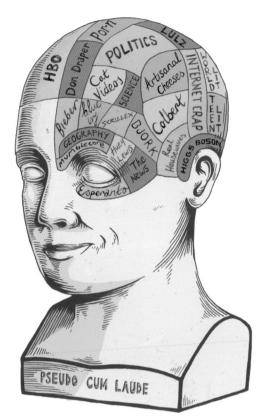

Comm. by Punch iPad Magazine.

Comm. for HSBC Liquid Magazine.

Comm. for Virgin Mobile.

Comm. by ShopSmart Magazine.

Comm. by Scientific American Magazine.

Comm. by SHOP Magazine.

Comm. for IB Magazine.

Neil Webb

début **art** • Illustrators, Photographers and Fine Artists Agents
30 Tottenham Street, London, W1T 4RJ. United Kingdom
Tel: 01144 20 7636 1064. Fax: 01144 20 7580 7017
The Coningsby Gallery • Tel: 01144 20 7636 7478

email: **info@debutart.com** • **www.debutart.com**

Comm. by CPO Agenda Magazine.

THE CATCHER IN THE RYE

Comm. for Art Battle LA.

Comm. for IB Magazine.

Comm. by The Financial Times.

début **art**

Comm. by Scholastic Publishing.

Self-initiated.

Comm. for Western Digital.

Self-initiated.

Sarah Howell

début **art** • Illustrators, Photographers and Fine Artists Agents
30 Tottenham Street, London, W1T 4RJ. United Kingdom
Tel: 01144 20 7636 1064. Fax: 01144 20 7580 7017
The Coningsby Gallery • Tel: 01144 20 7636 7478

email: **info@debutart.com** • **www.debutart.com**

début art

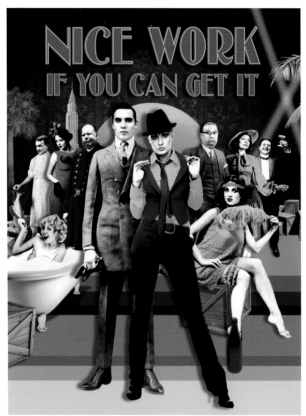

Poster concept for a Broadway Musical.

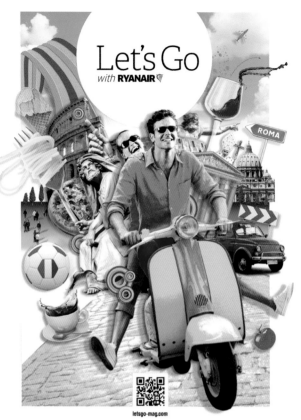

Comm. by Ryanair Inflight Magazine.

Comm. by Ryanair Inflight Magazine.

Comm. by The Economist Magazine.

Matt Herring

début **art** • Illustrators, Photographers and Fine Artists Agents
30 Tottenham Street, London, W1T 4RJ. United Kingdom
Tel: 01144 20 7636 1064. Fax: 01144 20 7580 7017
The Coningsby Gallery • Tel: 01144 20 7636 7478

email: **info@debutart.com** • **www.debutart.com**

début **art**

125

Comm. by GQ Magazine.

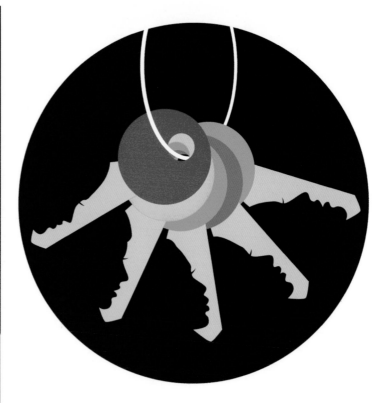

Comm. for SHOP Magazine.

'A Skulk of Foxes'. Self-initiated.

Comm. by GQ Magazine.

Patrick George

début **art** • Illustrators, Photographers and Fine Artists Agents
30 Tottenham Street, London, W1T 4RJ. United Kingdom
Tel: 01144 20 7636 1064. Fax: 01144 20 7580 7017
The Coningsby Gallery • Tel: 01144 20 7636 7478

email: **info@debutart.com** • **www.debutart.com**

début **art**

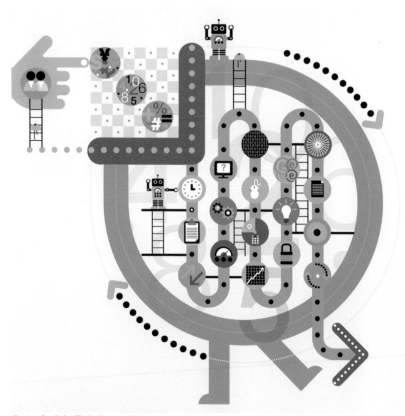

Comm. by Solo Flight Design Magazine.

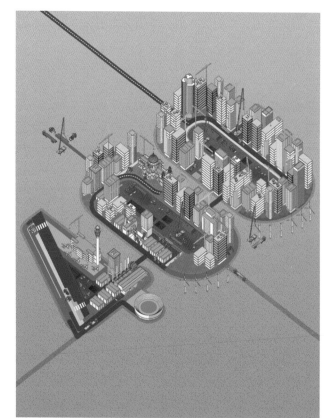

Comm. by McGraw Hill.

Comm. for BNP Paribas.

Comm. for Invesco.

Infomen

début **art** • Illustrators, Photographers and Fine Artists Agents
30 Tottenham Street, London, W1T 4RJ. United Kingdom
Tel: 01144 20 7636 1064. Fax: 01144 20 7580 7017
The Coningsby Gallery • Tel: 01144 20 7636 7478

email: **info@debutart.com** • **www.debutart.com**

début **art**

'I Heart Appz'. Self-initiated.

'Out Of The Darkness'. Self-initiated.

Jacey

début **art** • Illustrators, Photographers and Fine Artists Agents
30 Tottenham Street, London, W1T 4RJ. United Kingdom
Tel: 01144 20 7636 1064. Fax: 01144 20 7580 7017
The Coningsby Gallery • Tel: 01144 20 7636 7478

email: **info@debutart.com** • **www.debutart.com**

'Grind'. Self-initiated.

Comm. by The Financial Times.

Comm. by Esterson Associates.

Comm. by The Observer.

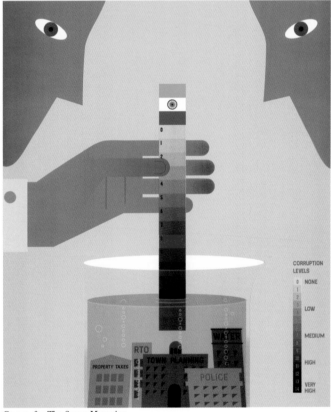

Comm. for The Scene Magazine.

Andrew Baker

début **art** • Illustrators, Photographers and Fine Artists Agents
30 Tottenham Street, London, W1T 4RJ. United Kingdom
Tel: 01144 20 7636 1064. Fax: 01144 20 7580 7017
The Coningsby Gallery • Tel: 01144 20 7636 7478

email: **info@debutart.com** • **www.debutart.com**

début art

Comm. by GQ Magazine.

Comm. for Hiscox.

Comm. for IKON Images.

Comm. by Billboard Magazine.

Nick Reddyhoff

début **art** • Illustrators, Photographers and Fine Artists Agents
30 Tottenham Street, London, W1T 4RJ. United Kingdom
Tel: 01144 20 7636 1064. Fax: 01144 20 7580 7017
The Coningsby Gallery • Tel: 01144 20 7636 7478

email: **info@debutart.com** • **www.debutart.com**

début **art**

Comm. by Canongate Books.

Comm. for Futurestep.

Comm. by Visit London.

Comm. for Beer Magazine.

Oscar Wilson

début **art** • Illustrators, Photographers and Fine Artists Agents
30 Tottenham Street, London, W1T 4RJ. United Kingdom
Tel: 01144 20 7636 1064. Fax: 01144 20 7580 7017
The Coningsby Gallery • Tel: 01144 20 7636 7478

email: **info@debutart.com** • **www.debutart.com**

début art

Comm. for Gola.

Self-initiated.

Comm. for Pub Scrawl 2012.

Tado

début **art** • Illustrators, Photographers and Fine Artists Agents
30 Tottenham Street, London, W1T 4RJ. United Kingdom
Tel: 01144 20 7636 1064. Fax: 01144 20 7580 7017
The Coningsby Gallery • Tel: 01144 20 7636 7478

email: **info@debutart.com** • **www.debutart.com**

début **art**

Comm. for Pitchfork Magazine.

Self-initiated.

Self-initiated.

'Game of Thrones'. Comm. by The New Yorker.

Vasili Zorin

début **art** • Illustrators, Photographers and Fine Artists Agents
30 Tottenham Street, London, W1T 4RJ. United Kingdom
Tel: 01144 20 7636 1064. Fax: 01144 20 7580 7017
The Coningsby Gallery • Tel: 01144 20 7636 7478

email: **info@debutart.com** • **www.debutart.com**

début art

Comm. by Disney.

Comm. by Moneyweek Magazine.

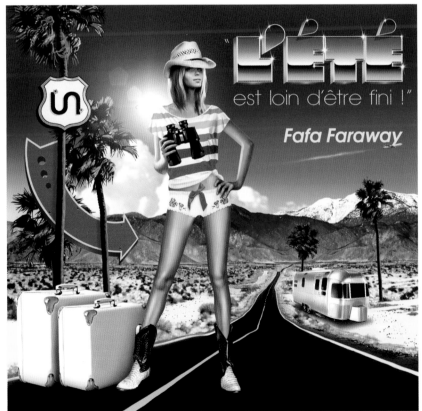

"L'ÉTÉ
est loin d'être fini !"

Fafa Faraway

Comm. for Undiz France.

TED BAKER
LONDON

Comm. for Ted Baker Eyewear.

ArnO

début **art**

ANNI
BETTS
illustration

{ **ANNIBETTS.COM**
312.415.1725

MELA BOLINAO **T** 212 689.7830 **F** 212 689.7829 www.mbartists.com

MB artists

VIRGINIA ALLYN

CONSTANZA BASALUZZO

VALENTINA BELLONI

MATTIA CERATO

RANDY CHEWNING

SERGIO DE GIORGI

VALERIA DOCAMPO

CAROLINA FARÍAS

PETER FRANCIS

VIVIANA GAROFOLI

ALESSIA GIRASOLE

GYNUX

JANNIE HO

IVANKE & LOLA

OLGA & ALEKSEY IVANOV

mb MB artists

ANNE KENNEDY

ANTHONY LEWIS

TAMMIE LYON

MIKE REED

MELA BOLINAO   **T** 212 689.7830   **F** 212 689.7829   www.mbartists.com

MB artists

MB artists

MELA BOLINAO   **T** 212 689.7830   **F** 212 689.7829   www.mbartists.com

IAN JOVEN

MARGEAUX LUCAS

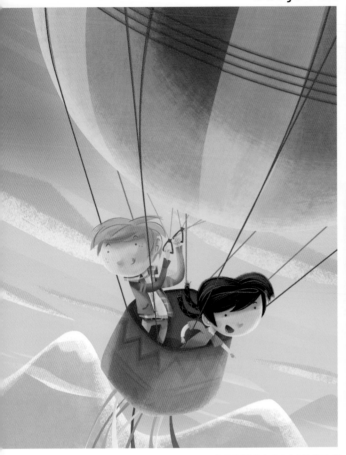

JOHN MANDERS

JULISSA MORA

HIROE NAKATA

MICK REID

Get on board!

KRISTIN SORRA

JENNIFER ZIVOIN

MB artists

MELA BOLINAO **T** 212 689.7830 **F** 212 689.7829 www.mbartists.com

www **p**ushart com

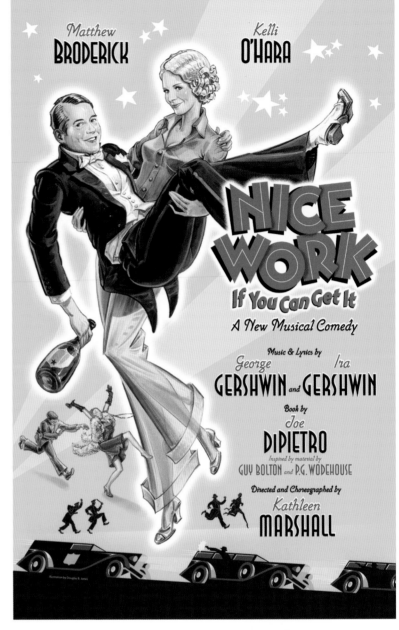

Mark Fredrickson
Gerald & Cullen Rapp
212-889-3337 www.rappart.com
info@rappart.com

BERNARD MAISNER
HAND - LETTERING
REPRESENTED BY
GERALD & CULLEN RAPP
212 - 889 - 3337
WWW.RAPPART.COM
INFO@RAPPART.COM

Bernard Maisner

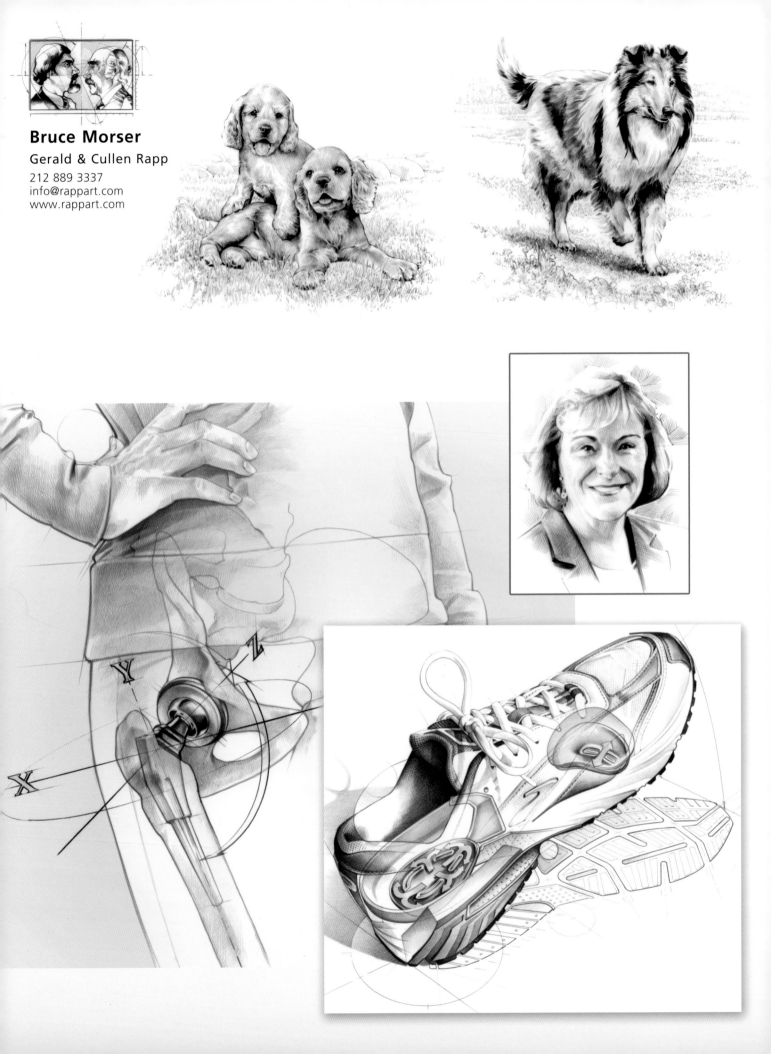

Bruce Morser

Gerald & Cullen Rapp

212 889 3337
info@rappart.com
www.rappart.com

Dan Page

Gerald &Cullen Rapp
212-889-3337
info@rappart.com
www.rappart.com
www.danpage.net

GERALD AND CULLEN RAPP
212 889 3337
WWW.RAPPART.COM
INFO@RAPPART.COM

Richard Mia

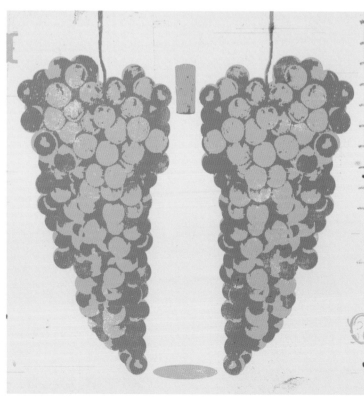

Jan Feindt
represented by
Gerald & Cullen Rapp
212.889.3337
janfeindt.de
www.rappart.com
info@rappart.com

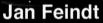

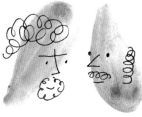

MARC ROSENTHAL REPRESENTED BY GERALD& CULLEN RAPP
212-889-3337 • INFO@RAPPART.COM
WWW.RAPPART.COM • WWW.MARC-ROSENTHAL.COM

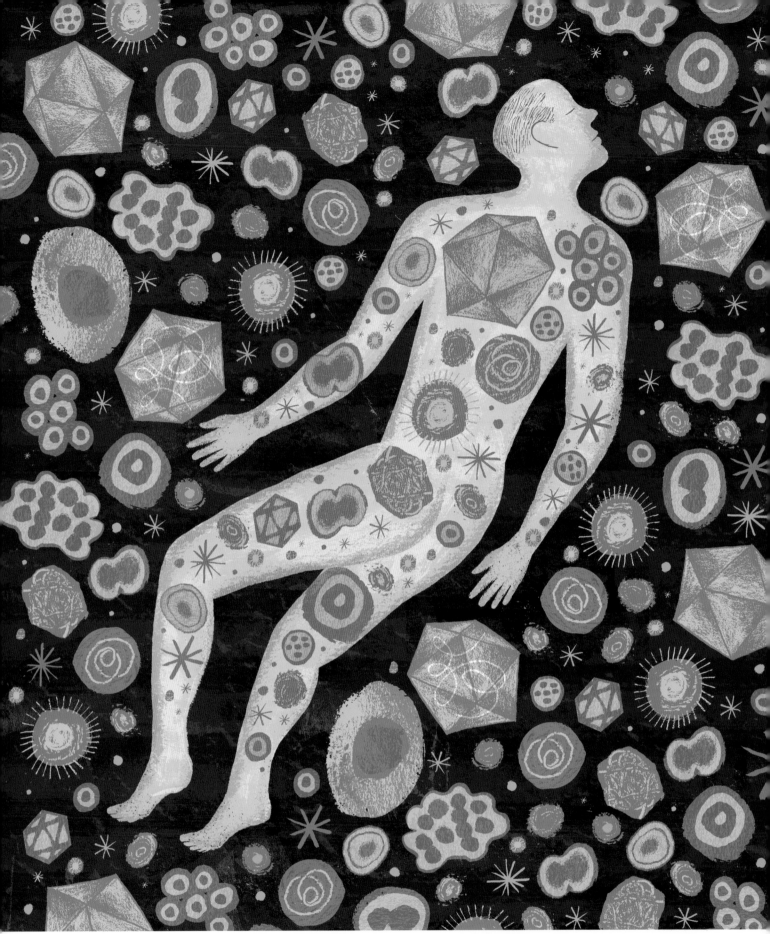

HANKOSUNA

Gerald & Cullen Rapp

212.889.2227

INFO@RAPPART.COM
WWW.RAPPART.COM
WWW.HANKOSUNA.COM

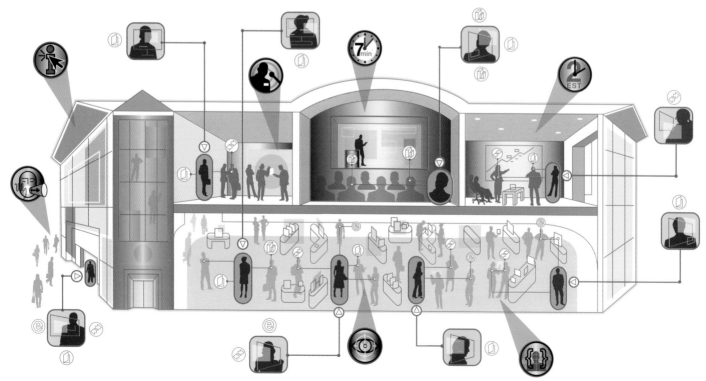

Michael Witte

Gerald & Cullen Rapp

212 889 3337
info@rappart.com
www.rappart.com

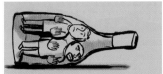

Robert Neubecker
Gerald & Cullen Rapp
212 889 3337
info@rappart.com
www.rappart.com/ neubecker.com

D A V I D
G O L D M A N
A G E N C Y

Since 1980 proudly

representing twelve of the

world's nicest and most intelligent

people, who just happen

to be extraordinary

Illustrators & Designers.

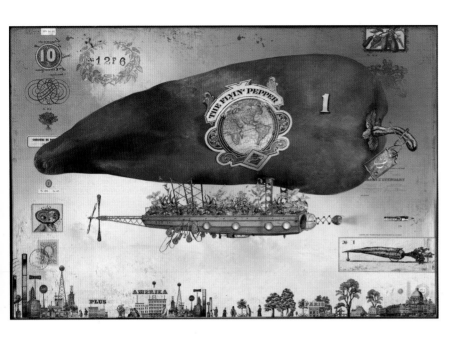

Bendell

bendellstudio.com

Falling   *Kai Creates*

A Holiday   *Apple/Tokyo*

American Girl

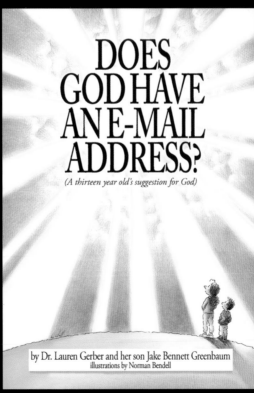

Dr. Lauren Gerber

Pets at Home   *Z Animation*

A Perfect Beach Day   *Z Animation*

JAMES YANG is proudly represented by DAVID GOLDMAN AGENCY

p: 212-807-6627 • **www.davidgoldmanagency.com** • dg@davidgoldmanagency.com • Twitter: @DGANYC

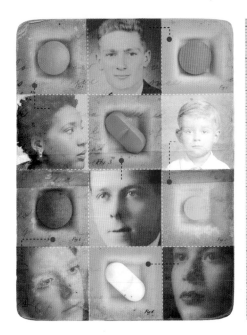

171

STEVE DININNO is proudly represented by DAVID GOLDMAN AGENCY

p: 212-807-6627 • **www.davidgoldmanagency.com** • dg@davidgoldmanagency.com • Twitter: @DGANYC

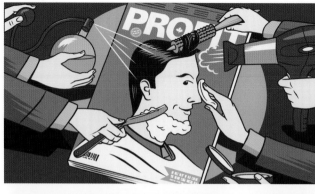

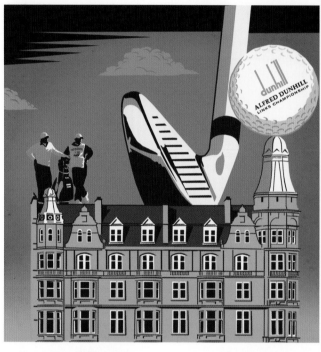

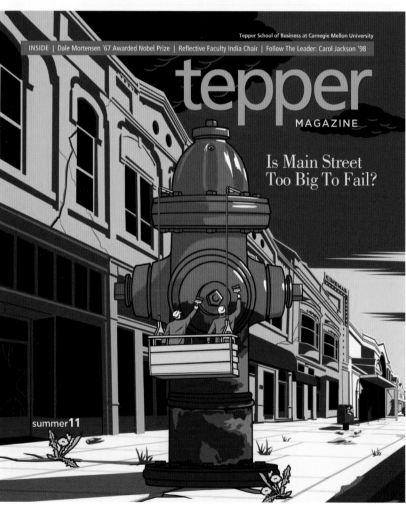

REPRESENTED BY TIDEPOOLREPS.COM

AMY DRESSER
DAUPE.COM

KIM JOHNSON

JON C. LUND

LINDGRENSMITH.COM **LINDGREN & SMITH** 212-397-7330

JIM SALVATI

MICHAEL ROBERTSON

MICHAEL PARASKEVAS

LINDGRENSMITH.COM

LINDGREN & SMITH

212-397-7330

JAMEY CHRISTOPH

ROBERT GANTT STEELE

SUSAN LEOPOLD

ROBERT WAGT

CHRIS O'LEARY

JOHN HOLCROFT

RICHARD FAUST

STEFANO VITALE

POL TURGEON

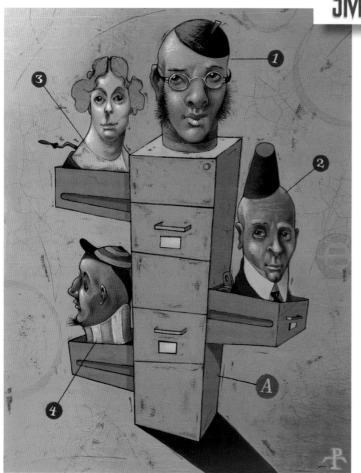

ROBERT RODRIGUEZ

JAMES BENTLEY

CHUCK PYLE

CHRIS LYONS

MILES HYMAN

JEFF BENNETT

CHRISTIANE BEAUREGARD

SUSAN CRAWFORD

GAYLE KABAKER

LINDGRENSMITH.COM

212-397-7330

REGAN DUNNICK

JEROME STUDER

24/7 STUDIO

COCO MASUDA

MARCELO CIPIS

LINDGRENSMITH.COM

LINDGREN & SMITH

212-397-7330

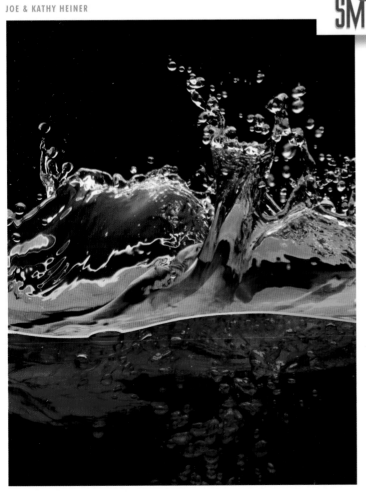

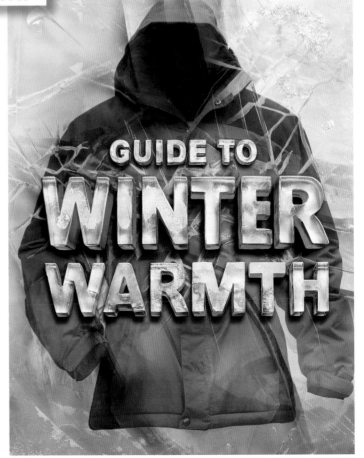

GUIDE TO WINTER WARMTH

185

RICHARD SOLOMON™
ARTISTS REPRESENTATIVE

Niklas Asker

Kent Barton

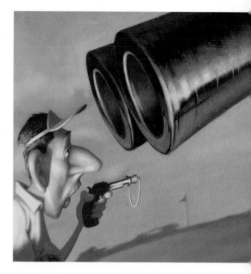

James Bennett

Tim Bower

Maria Corte Maidagan

Paul Cox

Kinuko Y. Craft

Eric Drooker

Michał Dziekan

110 E 30th Street
Suite 501
New York, NY 10016

212 223 9545 · 917 841 1333
richard@richardsolomon.com
www.richardsolomon.com

Thomas Ehretsmann

Jon Foster

Chris Gall

Rudy Gutierrez

Tyler Jacobson

David Johnson

Gary Kelley

Murray Kimber

Edward Kinsella III

Dongyun Lee

Gregory Manchess

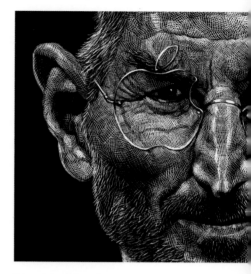

Ricardo Martínez

John Mattos

Goñi Montes

Yan Nascimbene

Tran Nguyen

CF Payne

Bill Sanderson

110 E 30th Street
Suite 501
New York, NY 10016

212 223 9545 · 917 841 1333
richard@richardsolomon.com
www.richardsolomon.com

son Seiler

Douglas Smith

Mark T. Smith

uy Stauber

Chase Stone

Mark Summers

hris Whetzel

Andrew R. Wright

Ted Wright

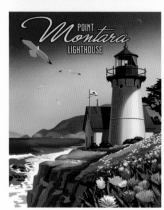

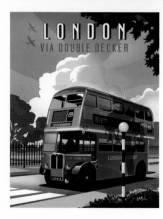

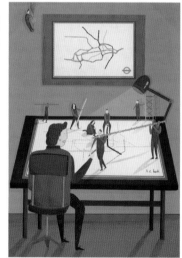

w: www.folioart.co.uk
e: info@folioart.co.uk
t: +44 (0)20 7242 9562

Folio Illustration Agency
36 Years of brightening up the world

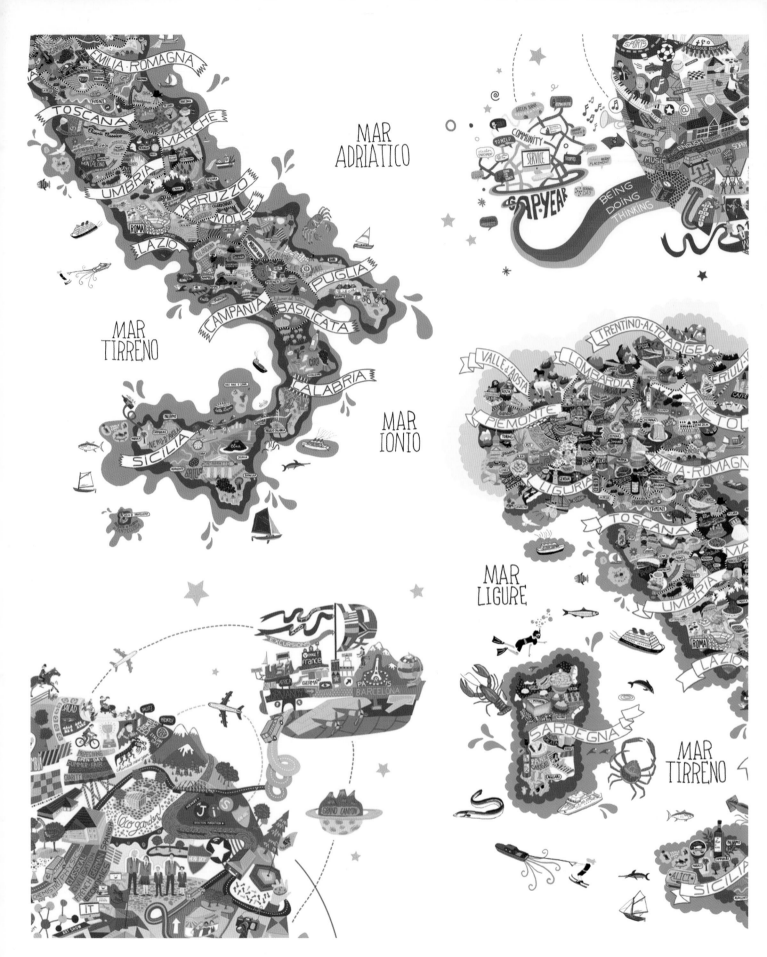

w: www.folioart.co.uk
e: info@folioart.co.uk
t: +44 (0)20 7242 9562

Antoine Corbineau

w: www.folioart.co.uk
e: info@folioart.co.uk
t: +44 (0)20 7242 9562

Alex Green

Andy Watt

Anne Sharp

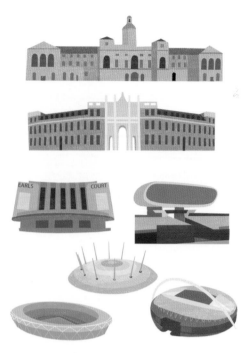

Britta Stenhouse

Clear As Mud

David Biskup

Jill Barthorpe

w: www.folioart.co.u
e: info@folioart.co.uk
t: +44 (0)20 7242 9562

Various

Daniel Atanasov

David Juniper

Ella Cohen

Gabriel Corbera

Iker Spozio

James Gilleard

w: www.folioart.co.uk
e: info@folioart.co.uk
t: +44 (0)20 7242 9562

Various

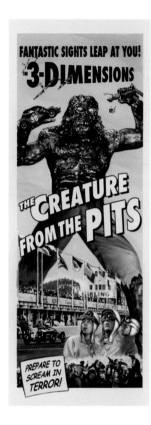

w: www.folioart.co.uk
e: info@folioart.co.uk
t: +44 (0)20 7242 9562

Bruce Emmett

w: www.folioart.co.uk
e: info@folioart.co.uk
t: +44 (0)20 7242 9562

David Lawrence

w: www.folioart.co.uk
e: info@folioart.co.uk
t: +44 (0)20 7242 9562

Lisa Evans

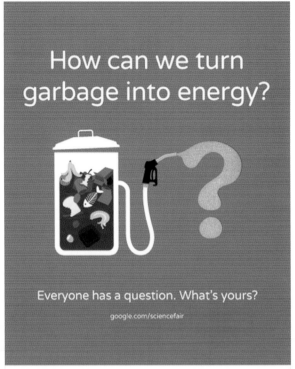

How can we turn garbage into energy?

Everyone has a question. What's yours?

google.com/sciencefair

Google Science Fair 2012

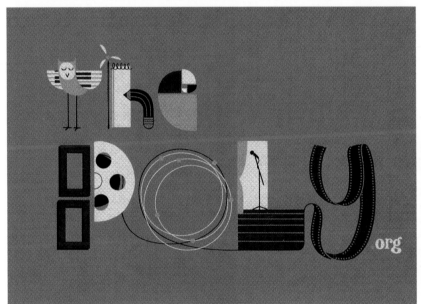

thevine✴
Marketing with SOUL

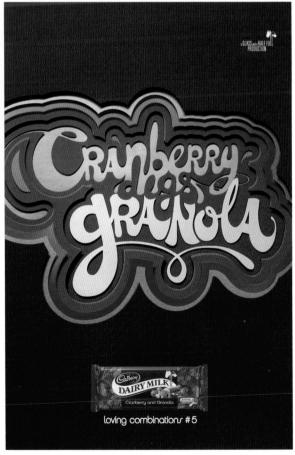

w: www.folioart.co.uk
e: info@folioart.co.uk
t: +44 (0)20 7242 9562

Nick Radford

w: www.folioart.co.uk
e: info@folioart.co.uk
t: +44 (0)20 7242 9562

Nicola Meiring

w: www.folioart.co.uk
e: info@folioart.co.uk
t: +44 (0)20 7242 9562

Owen Davey

SAPA
VIETNAM

FRANCE
CHAMONIX

BALI
INDONESIA

AMSTERDAM
THE NETHERLANDS

VIETNAM
HA LONG BAY

CHARLES
FRAZIER

NIGHTWOODS

Rui Ricardo

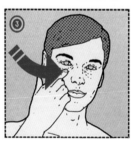

w: www.folioart.co.uk
e: info@folioart.co.uk
t: +44 (0)20 7242 9562

Son of Alan

Joe Petagno

Josie Jo

Kate Evans

Laurie Stansfield

Mark Dickson

Nick Purser

w: www.folioart.co.uk
e: info@folioart.co.uk
t: +44 (0)20 7242 9562

Various

Nicola Pontin

Piero Corva

Roger Watt

Siku

Sydney Couldridge

Tony Meeuwissen

w: www.folioart.co.uk
e: info@folioart.co.uk
t: +44 (0)20 7242 9562

Various

w: www.folioart.co.uk
e: info@folioart.co.uk
t: +44 (0)20 7242 9562

Toby Leigh

Jui Ishida

Shelly Hehenberger

208

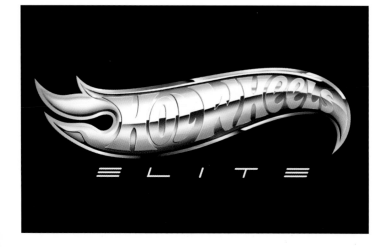

209

dave **titus**

www.dasgrup.com · carrie perlow · 310.374.1575

BUGLING

MERIT BADGE HANDBOOK

CAPTAIN MORGANS PRIVATE STOCK **EXTREME GROUP/HALIFAX**

Brian Love

Marina Seoane

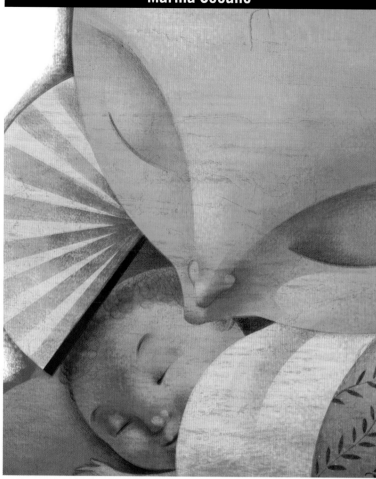

Leland Klanderman

Karen Wolcott

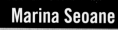

BLASCO CREATIVE ARTISTS

Rolf Asymmetric Illustration

Larry Martin

Jeff Faerber

Howard McWilliam

BLASCO CREATIVE ARTISTS

ANDREA **CASTELLANI**

LUIS **TINOCO**

KATIA **DE CONTI**

PAULE **TRUDEL BELLEMARE**

MAX **KOSTENKO**

MARK **DYLAN**

DIEGO **DIAZ**

BILLMUND

GARY **VENN**

BESS **HARDING**

MARIA CRISTINA **COSTA**

SANTIAGO **GRASSO**

LUIGI RUSSO **SAS**

MARCELO **BADARI**

LUISPA **SALMON**

OLGA **WEBER**

ZLATKO **DRCAR**

TONY **SIGLEY**

PABLO MORENO **CALLES**

EVA **GARCES**

Lemonade
illustration agency

Representing **70 Illustrators, Animators** and **Storyboard Artists** who are serving innovative clients in all locations across the World, however hectic the deadline.

t : +44 (0) 7891 390750
e : info@lemonadeillustration.com
w : www.lemonadeillustration.com

LONDON& NEW YORK

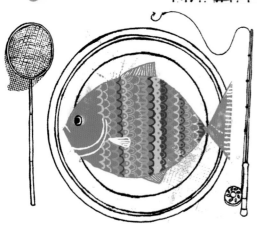

illustration agency

REPRESENTING
DAVID **BROADBENT**

t : +44 (0) 7891 390750
e : info@lemonadeillustration.com
w : www.lemonadeillustration.com

LONDON&
NEW YORK

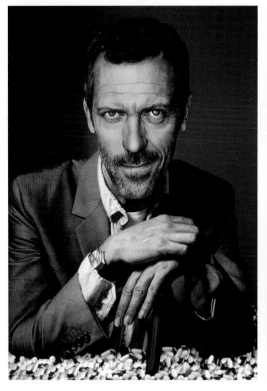

Lemonade
illustration agency

illustration agency

DEVILISH, WINGED AND DANGEROUS!

DEMON STRIKE

ANDREW NEWBOUND

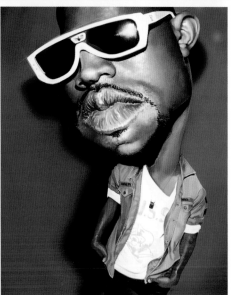

Lemonade

illustration agency

REPRESENTING

LUKE **WATSON**

t : +44 (0) 7891 390750
e : info@lemonadeillustration.com
w : www.lemonadeillustration.com

LONDON&
NEW YORK

Lemonade
illustration agency

REPRESENTING
CHRIS **DICKASON**

t : +44 (0) 7891 390750
e : info@lemonadeillustration.com
w : www.lemonadeillustration.com

LONDON&
NEW YORK

Lemonade
illustration agency

REPRESENTING
HELEN **HUANG**

t : +44 (0) 7891 390750
e : info@lemonadeillustration.com
w : www.lemonadeillustration.com

LONDON&
NEW YORK

HOLY COW

garyswift.com

illustration agency

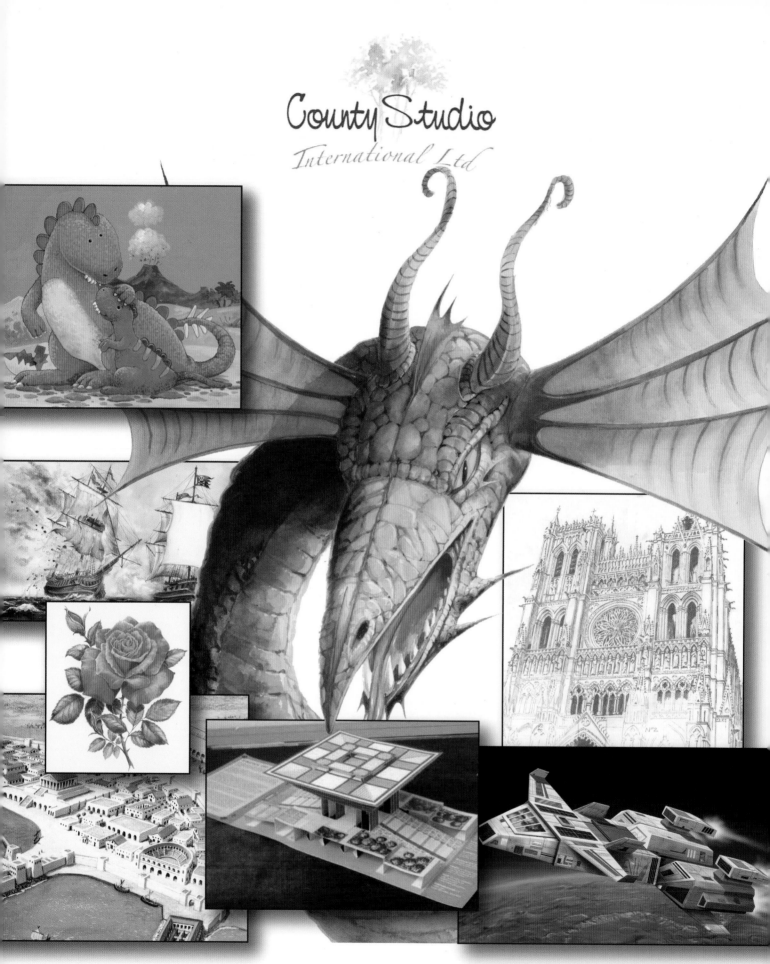

County Studio
International Ltd

Christer Eriksson

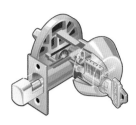
Michael Jones

Colin Poole

Joe McDermott

Jeff Pollard

Kelly Pierce

Dave Ember

AP* ENVIRONMENTAL SCIENCE

Kelly Hume

Paul Borchers

Jason Lynch

Dean Kennedy

Sue Rother

Juan Alvarez

Greg Lamb

COMPS

Kym Foster

artagent.com

Bruce Hutchison

Tricia Martin

John Fraser

Darren Gygi

Michael Hogue

Tim Jessell

Gary Locke

Scott Dawson

Ezra Tucker

Sudi McCollum

Amy Ning

Liz Sanders Agency

Telephone: (509) 993-6400   *there's more at* LizSanders.com   Facsimile: (509) 466-5400

illustrationOnLine.com
illustration and animation

215.232.6666 **illustration**OnLine.com DEBORAH WOLFE LTD

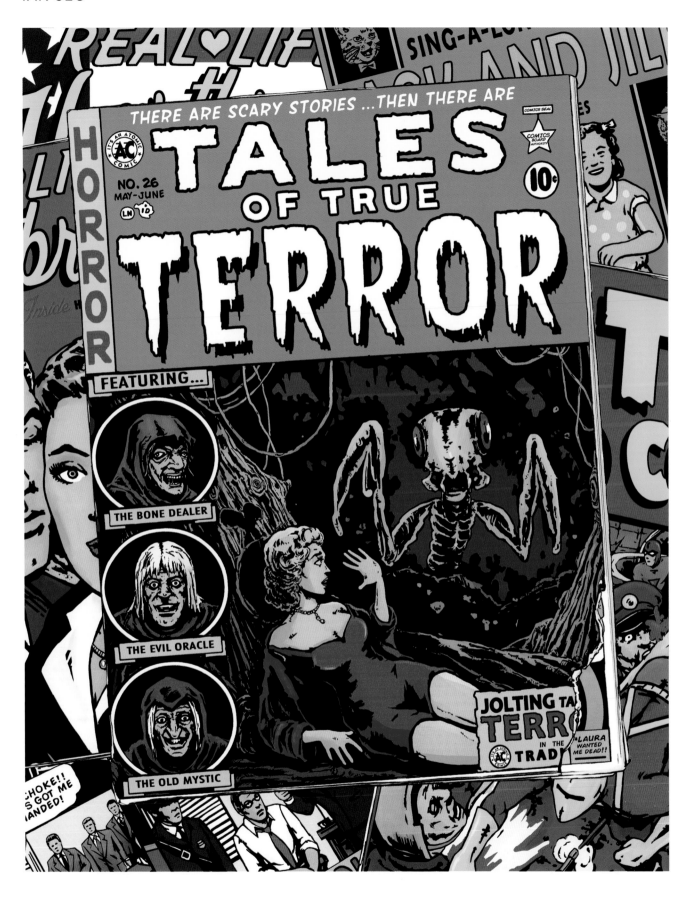

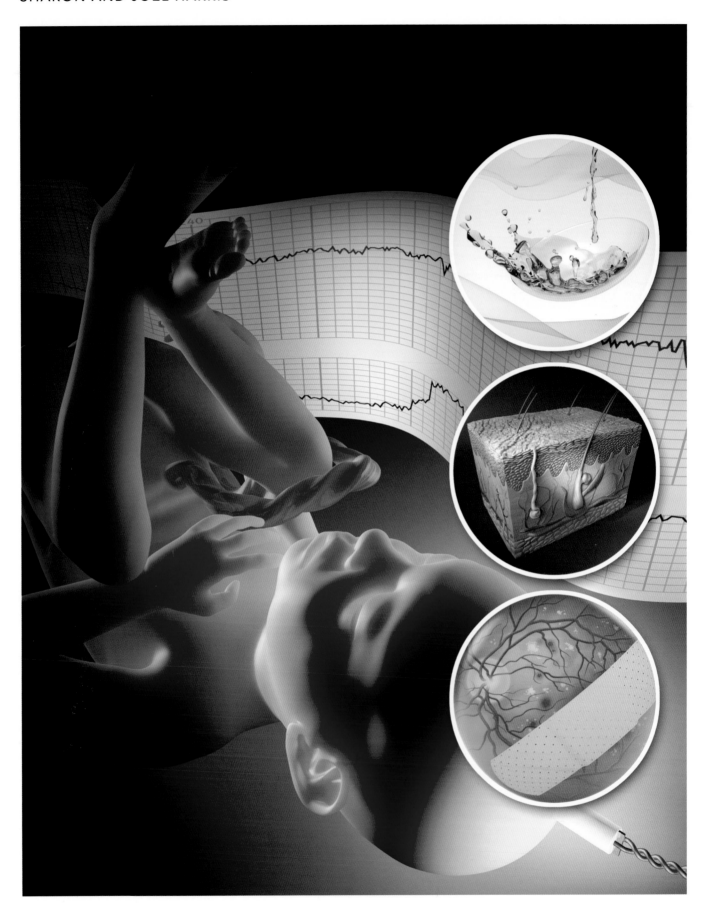

DAN McGEEHAN

JOHN SCHREINER

GERAD TAYLOR

JT MORROW

MICHAEL GARLAND

MARK COLLINS

ROSS JONES

AMY WUMMER

JESSE REISCH

TED HAMMOND

BOB OSTROM

Christina A. Tugeau

(757) 221-0666
www.catugeau.com

Cathy Gendron

Ann Iosa

Laura Logan

Sarah Beise

Melissa Iwai

Christina A. Tugeau

(757) 221-0666
www.catugeau.com

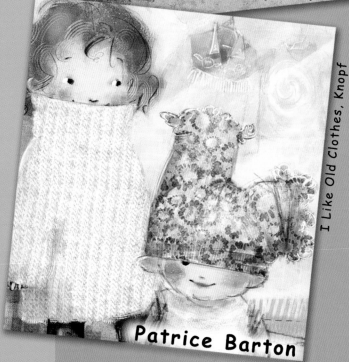
Joanne Friar

Kelly Kennedy

Meryl Treatner

Patrice Barton

I Like Old Clothes, Knopf

Cheryl Kirk Noll

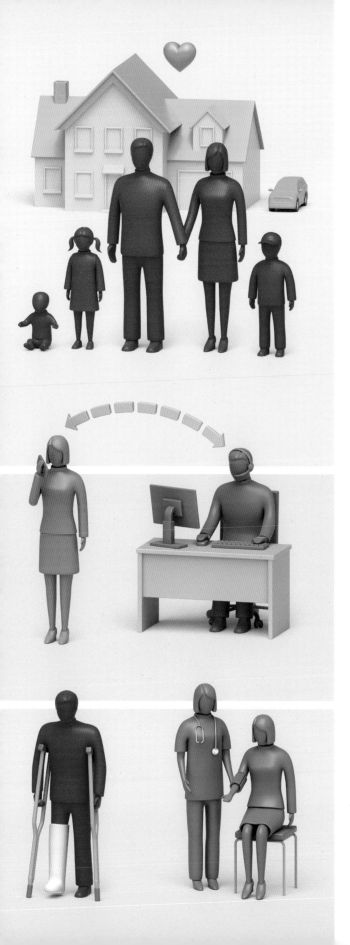

US OPEN

2012

HOPS: SAAZ NOBLE HOPS

MALTS: TWO-ROW PALE MALTS, MUNICH, MALTED AND UNMALTED WHEAT

The "LOST" BEER

SPECIAL ingredients: BREWED WITH CORIANDER AND SALT

SAMUEL ADAMS®

FAT JACK

MALTS: SAMUEL ADAMS TWO-ROW PALE MALT BLEND, CARAMEL 60, SPECIAL B, AND SMOKED MALT

SPECIAL Ingredients: REAL Pumpkin, CINNAMON, GINGER, NUTMEG, ALLSPICE

HOPS: EAST KENT GOLDINGS AND FUGGLES

DOUBLE PUMPKIN
ALE BREWED WITH PUMPKIN AND SPICES
8.5% ALC./VOL. | 1PT. 6FL. OZ.

ENJOY NOW OR AGE IT TO FURTHER DEVELOP RICH AND UNIQUE FLAVORS
BREWED BY THE BOSTON BEER COMPANY, BOSTON, MA., CINCINNATI, OH. AND BREINIGSVILLE, PA. VISIT US AT 30 GERMANIA ST, BOSTON, MA 02130 OR CALL 1-888-661-2337.
© THE BOSTON BEER COMPANY

GOVERNMENT WARNING: (1) ACCORDING TO THE SURGEON GENERAL, WOMEN SHOULD NOT DRINK ALCOHOLIC BEVERAGES DURING PREGNANCY BECAUSE OF THE RISK OF BIRTH DEFECTS. (2) CONSUMPTION OF ALCOHOLIC BEVERAGES IMPAIRS YOUR ABILITY TO DRIVE A CAR OR OPERATE MACHINERY, AND MAY CAUSE HEALTH PROBLEMS.

9215

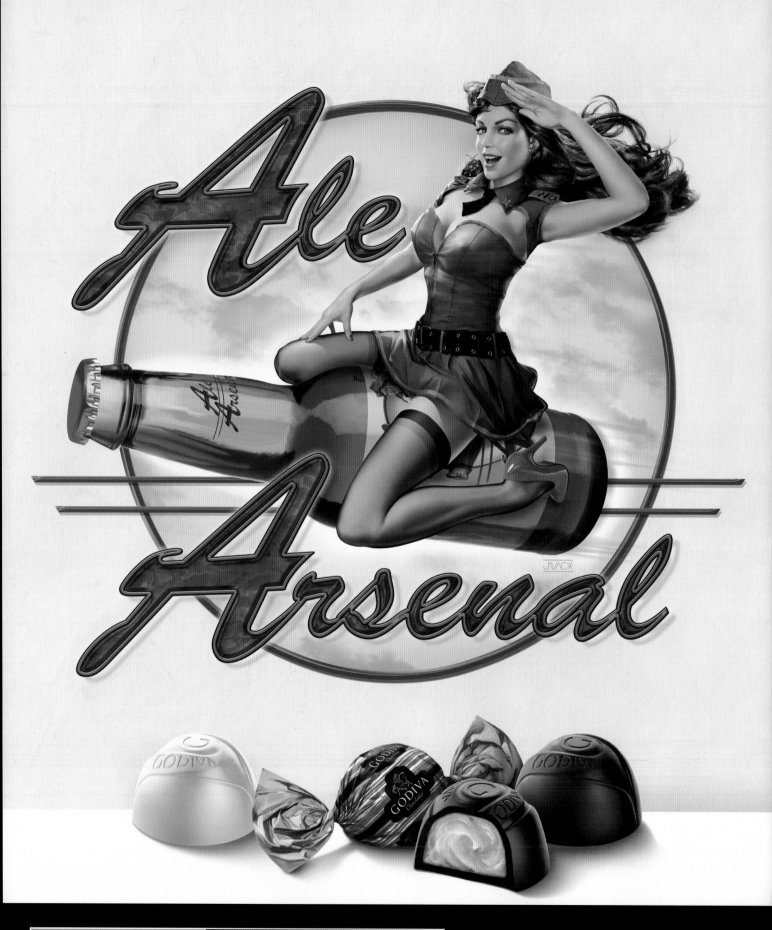

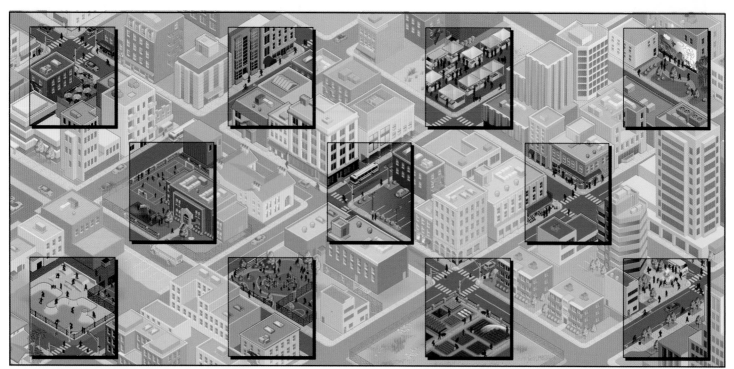

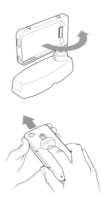

CIRCUS UNDER THE STARS

A — Architecture

B — Bio Shock 2

C — Cherry Cola

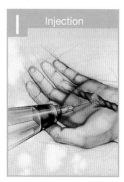

D — Dog & Cat

E — Elmo

F — Floor Plan

G — Guitar Hero

H — Haircare

I — Injection

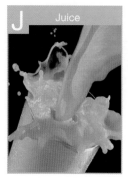

J — Juice

K — Kiwi

L — Logos

M — Maps

N — Nice

Find Your Solution
www.aareps.com

ph. 212.682.2462

AA REPS
Creative for interactive, motion & print

info@aareps.com

O — Ozzy

P — Pin Up

Q — Q-Omega

R — Racecars

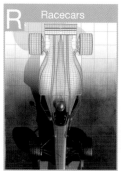

S — Sub

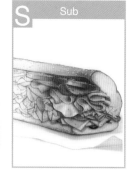

T — Tea

U — Umbrella

V — Volcano

W — Waterslide

X — X-Ray

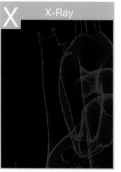

Y — Yellow Leathers

Z — Zoo

Annie-France Giroud

Tony Randazzo

ARTISTIC
IMAGE

EASY DRINKING CRISPER FRESHER

DESIGN AND FX FOR BROaADCAST + PRINT

Katarina Voloder

Marcel Laverdet

Darren Whittington

Pastiche

Volkswagen Front Assist. It knows what's ahead.

Das Auto.

Big Al Gruswitz

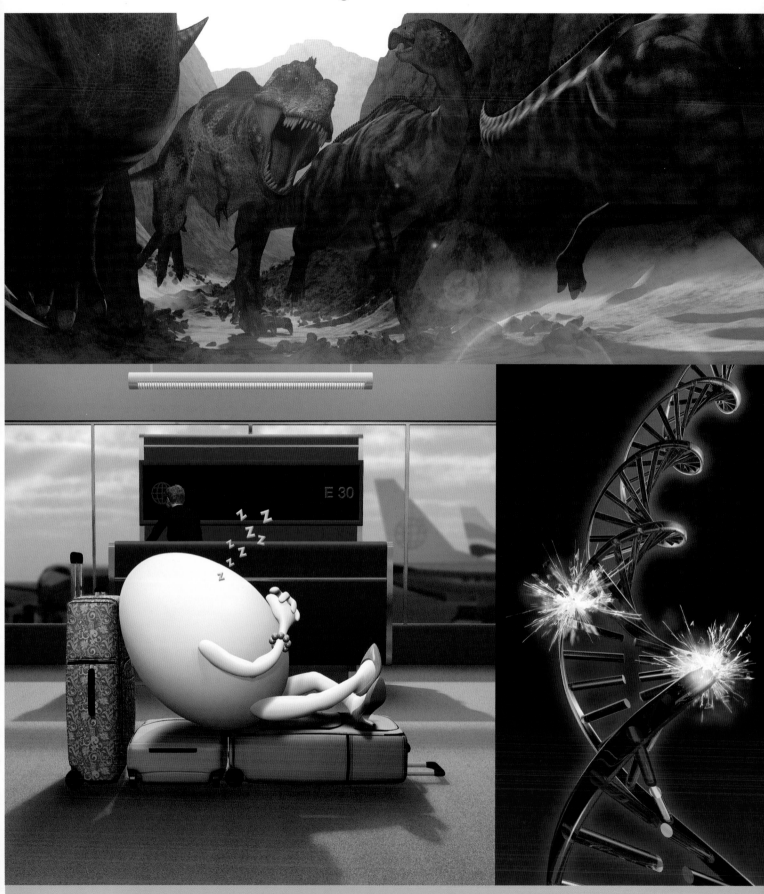

Thodoris Tibilis

Giovannina Colalillo

Curt Walstead

Geo Parkin

Reginald Polynice

Tim Frame Design

Rick Grayson

Alan Male

Jim Steck

Kent Gamble

Craig Zuckerman

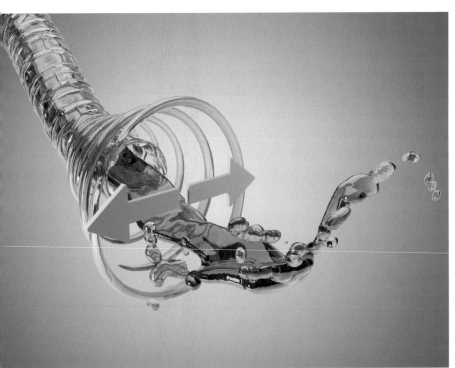
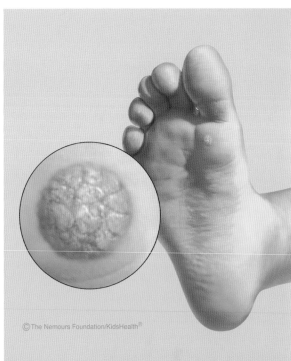

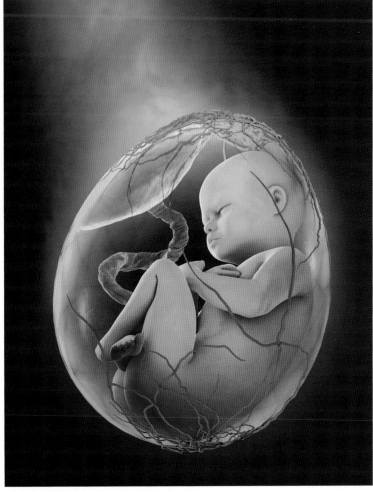

AA REPS

Since 1920

Creative for interactive, motion & print

Find Your Solution
www.aareps.com

ph.212.682.2462
fx.212.582.0090
info@aareps.com

Randy Glass

www.RandyGlassStudio.com

David Semple

Matt Zang

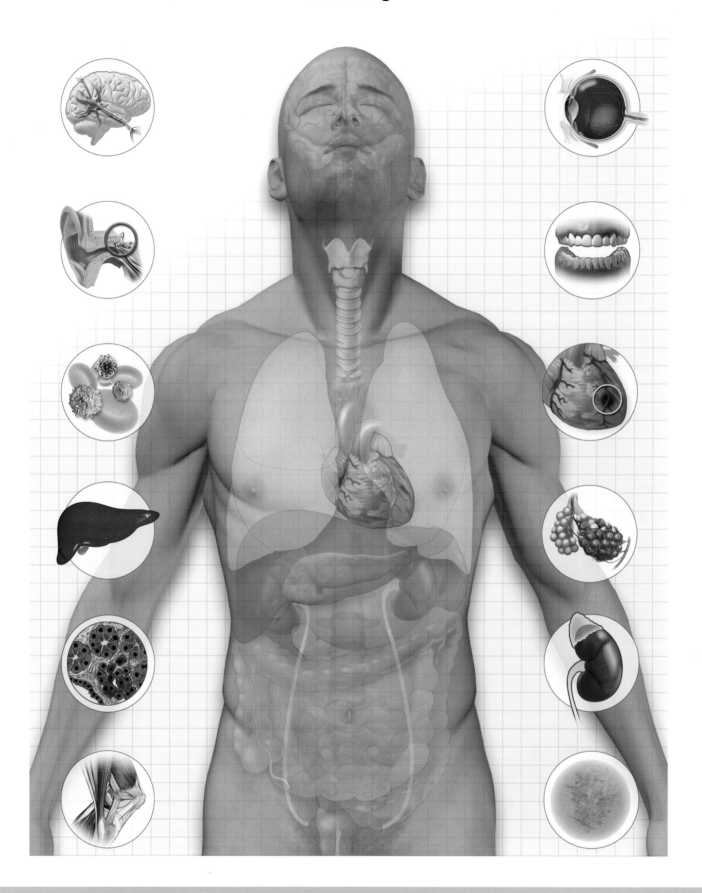

Bonnie Hofkin

Jerry LoFaro

NATHANIEL WEST

MARIANO DIAZ

HUGO MARTIN

KINO SCIALABBA

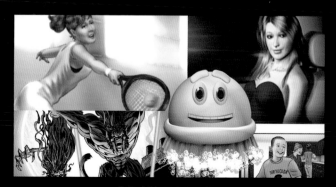

BRAINFOREST

JP TARGETE

A

ACTION ARTISTS

▸ *an agency for storyboard & conceptual artists*

PH.
323 337 4666

WWW.
ACTION-ARTISTS.COM

E.
BETH@ACTION-ARTISTS.COM

SHANE L. JOHNSON ILLUSTRATION

ILLUSTRATION   COMICS   STORYBOARDS   CHARACTER DESIGN

Tyson Mangelsdorf

Illustration

Agents

Stacey Endress   Karen Kaller

Juliette Lott   Mike Cowley

illustrationweb.com   23 Ohio Street

973.763.1712   Maplewood

howdy@illustrationweb.com   NJ 07040

Belicta Castelbarco

Wai

Kavel Rafferty

Hannah Davies

Yordanka Poleganova ▶

Turine Tran
Adam Larkum

Jason Hawkins
Bill Greenhead

 Fernando Juarez

illustrationweb.com   howdy@illustrationweb.com   973.763.1712

Illustration

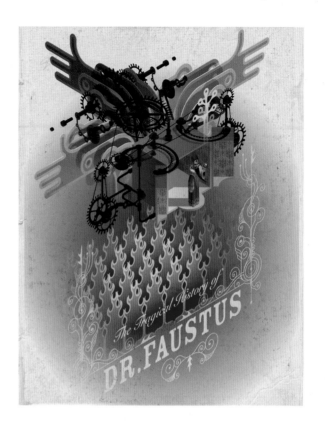

Steven Pattison

Mark Oliver

Dennis Juan Ma

BoomArtwork ▶

Lucia Emanuela Curzi
Bec Winnel

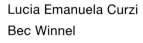 Nuno DaCosta

Miss Led
Ward Nipper

Gail Armstrong

Shailesh Khandeparkar

Paul Holland

Heather Landis ▶

illustrationweb.com　　howdy@illustrationweb.com　　973.763.1712

Reimagine
Chris Boyd

 Ignite

Derek Bacon
Cube

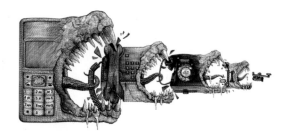

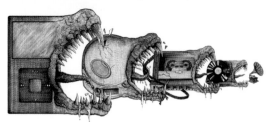

Hannah Firmin

Richard Phipps

Philip Bannister

Rosie Sanders

Lauren Mortimer ▶

illustrationweb.com   howdy@illustrationweb.com   973.763.1712

Timothy Banks

Leonardo Meschini

WilkinSon
STUDIOS, INC
International Agents for Illustration

www.wilkinsonstudios.com
630.549.0504

Jared Osterhold

Estudio Haus

Roger Stewart

Drew Rose

Francesca D'Ottavi

Gina Pfleegor

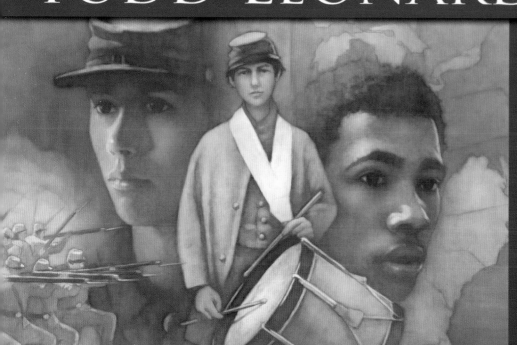

TODD LEONARDO ILLUSTRATION

Illustration by: Kurt Huggins and Zelda Devon

JOSÉE BISAILLON

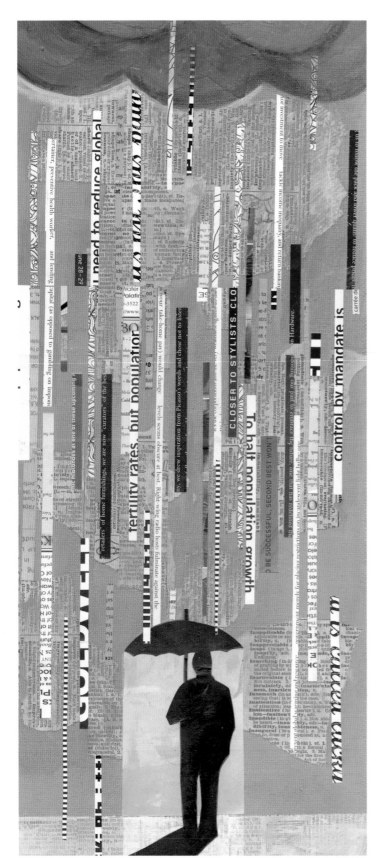

ELIZABETH ROSEN

BEPPE GIACOBBE

SALLY VITSKY

194 THIRD AVE NYC 10003 (212)475-0440
MORGAN GAYNIN INC MORGANGAYNIN.COM

CARLO STANGA

NANETTE BIERS

PETE RYAN

PATTI MOLLICA

SUSAN GAL

RENÉ MILOT

Art On The Ridge

8005 Greenwood Ave N. Seattle, WA 98103
(206)510-3421 info@artontheridge.com
www.artontheridge.com

Alyson Jones

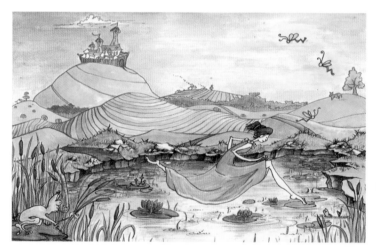

Priscilla Neilson

Nicole Monahan

Andy Hoyos

Steve Feldman

www.stevefeldman.com   541-975-3333   steve@stevefeldman.com

PO Box 948 La Grande OR 97850   See also Directory of Illustration 28 pg 340

Scholastic

Workman Publishing

Constellation Brands, Inc.

E. J. Gallo Winery

Workman Publishing

Cost Plus World Market

William H. Sadlier, Inc.

EVE STECCATI

PICTORIAL MAPS

PHONE: 510.339.0182   PORTFOLIO: stcreative.com/eve.html   EMAIL: eve@stcreative.com

Castel del Monte

Villa Capra "La Rotonda"

Basilica di San Marco

Castello Pepoli

Arco di Settimio Severo

Tempio della Concordia

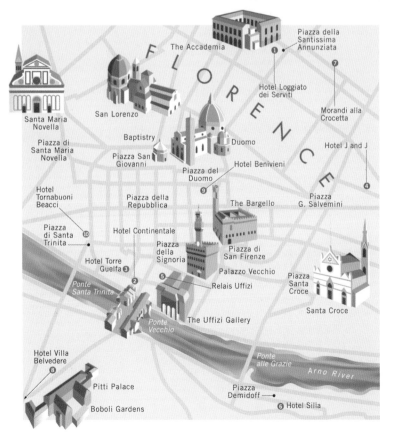

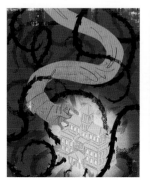
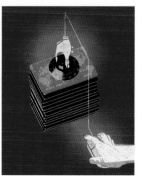

Josée Morin Art Studio

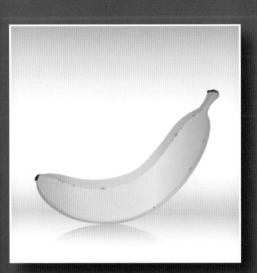

Ed Bray

www.edbrayillustrations.com

t:978-970-0558 c: 651-587-0099

edbrayillustration@verizon.net

"Pecos Bill Rides the Tornado" | *for Scholastic*

BILL CIGLIANO | children's publishing

www.billcigliano.com | *773 . 973 . 0062*

Barack Obama | for Education Next Magazine

"The End of Conversation" | *for Briefings Magazine*

Residential Architecture Firms | "Planning for a Better Future" | for the AIA

BILL CIGLIANO | personalities & concepts

www.billcigliano.com | 773 . 973 . 0062

·NEWBOLD·

801.274.2407
GREGNEWBOLD.COM

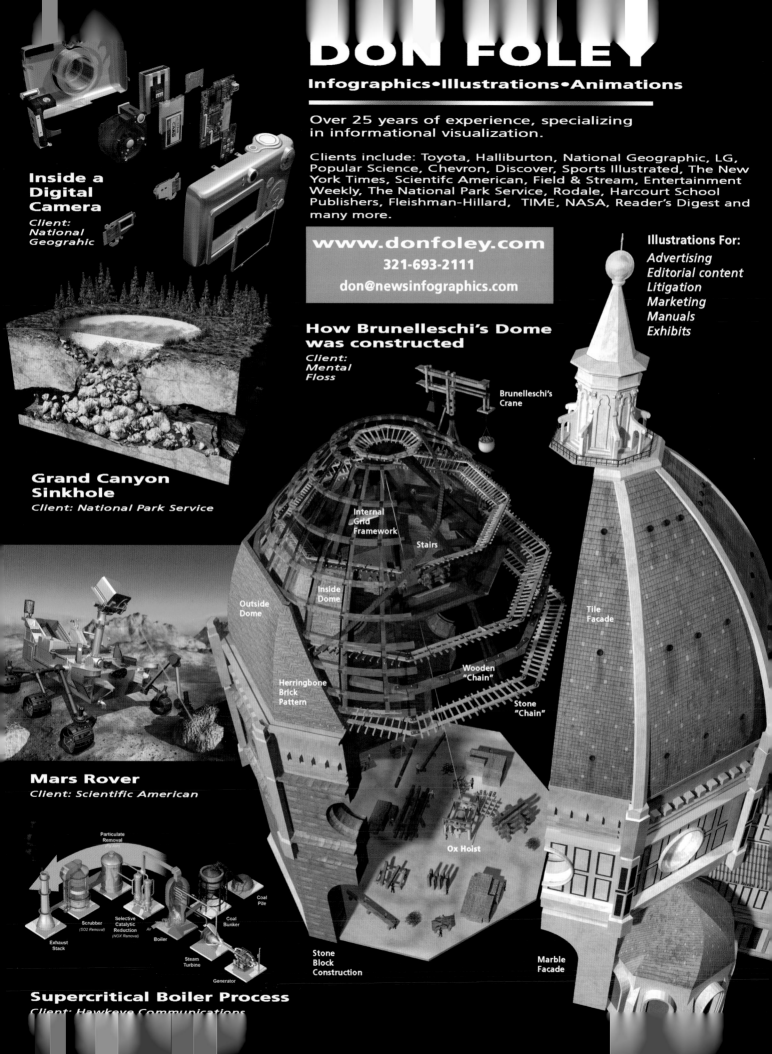

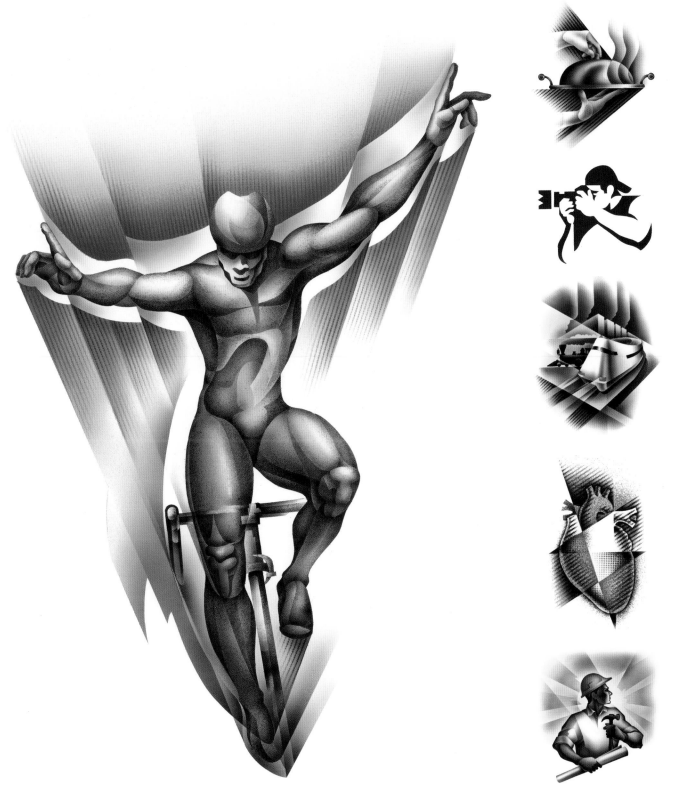

Boris Lyubner   435-649-2129    **.com**

AMY DeVOOGD ILLUSTRATION
www.devoogd.com **608.692.3386** amy@devoogd.com

X Mark Todd
marktoddillustration.com
626-836-2210

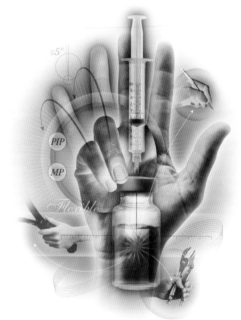

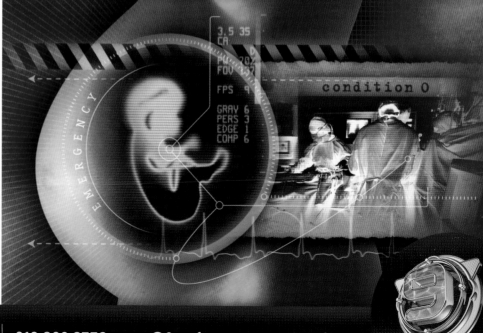

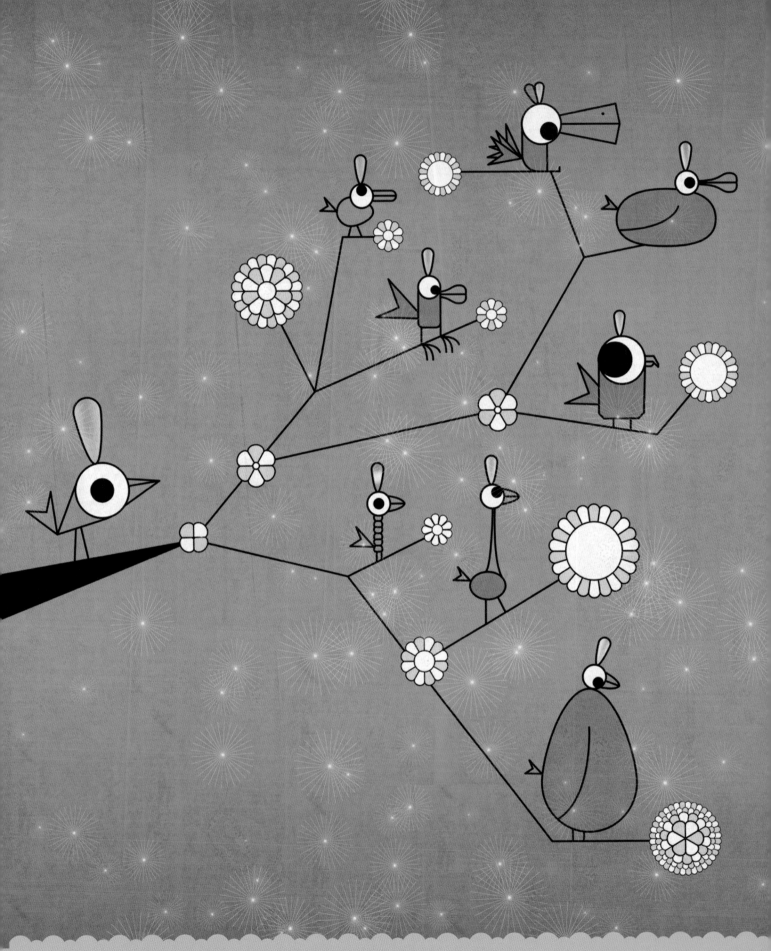

JOHN HERSEY: 415 302 9401   JOHN@HERSEY.COM   TWITTER: @JOHNDUCKFACE   ILLOZ: ILLOZ.COM/JOHNHERSEY

melinda beck ✳ 347.463.2306 ✳ melindabeck.com

Joseph Kelly

EMAIL: JOSEPHKELLY@ME.COM
WEB: ILLUSTRATEDBYJOSEPHKELLY.COM
PHONE: (415) 731-3436

daryll collins humorous illustration

JONATHAN KOELSCH
ILLUSTRATOR

405·641·2222

jkillustrator.com   character design | advertising | editorial | children's books   jk@jkillustrator.com

Clients from top to bottom include

Sadlier Publishing NYC,
Tempur-Pedic Mattresses (Trade),
Delightmare Publishing,
Questing Vole Press.

RAYNE BEAUDOIN ILLUSTRATION

Tel: (206) 463-2607
23309 Wax Orchard Rd SW, Vashon Island, WA 98070
See more work online at www.raynebeaudoin.com

CHARACTER DEVELOPMENT * EDITORIAL * CHILDRENS * LICENSE * ADVERTISING

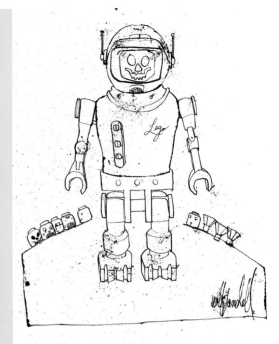

SCOTT GANDELL | (626) 262 - 3909 | WWW.SCOTTGANDELL.COM

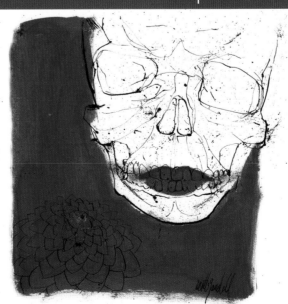

357

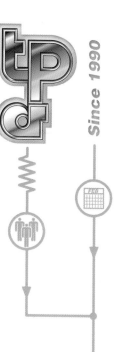

Steve Nichol
309•263•8792
tpainc@mtco.com
www.tpainc.ws
technical writing • editing

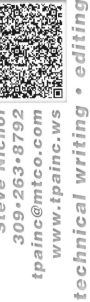

KAC Corp.

Walker Process Equipment

Shaver MFG.

Meridian MFG.

Whether it's technical writing or illustrations for your manuals, patent applications, or marketing materials, we are here to meet your creative and technical needs.

Technical Publication Associates, Inc.

Aa aguacate	Bb berenjena	Cc coco	CHch champiñón	Dd durazno
Ee espinaca	Ff fresa	Gg guayaba	Hh habichuelas	Ii
Jj jalapeño	Kk kiwi	Ll limón	ll	Mm mango

FRUTAS Y VERDURAS | UN ABECEDARIO

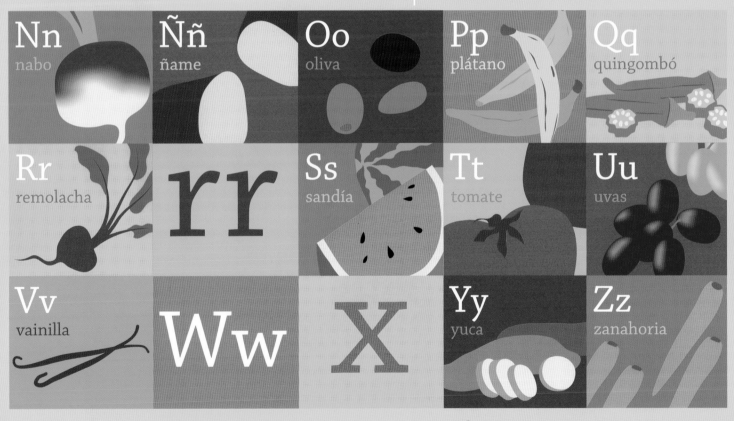

Nn nabo	Ññ ñame	Oo oliva	Pp plátano	Qq quingombó
Rr remolacha	rr	Ss sandía	Tt tomate	Uu uvas
Vv vainilla	Ww	X	Yy yuca	Zz zanahoria

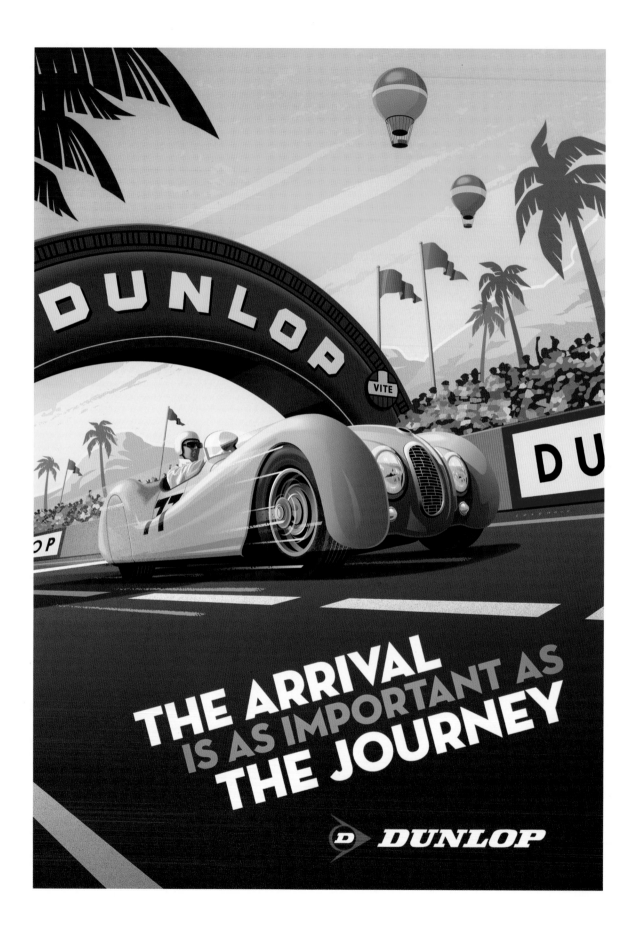

PETRE PASPALOVSKI

Rob De Bank

PH 310 519.1357   robdebank.com   CELL 310 350-1832

367

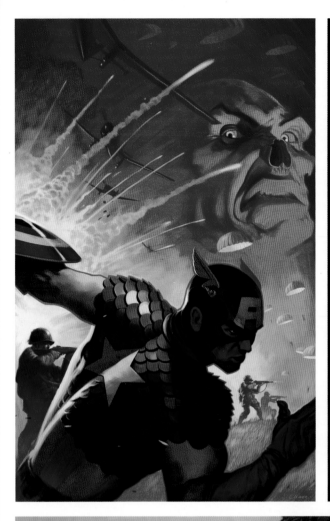

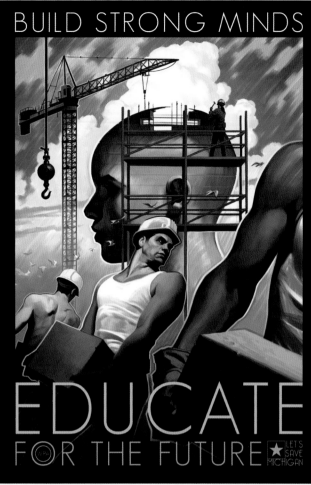

BUILD STRONG MINDS

EDUCATE
FOR THE FUTURE

Alex Beeching

JOHN MANTHA

416 778 5089

john.mantha@sympatico.ca

johnmantha.com

Jack Pittman

919-785-1966

www.jptoonist.com

jack@jackpittman.net

Awarded Best in Advertising Illustration and Best in Magazine Feature Illustration in the National Cartoonists Society's 50th, 53rd, and 59th Annual Reuben Awards.

Mark Thoburn
illustrative designer

540-247-3124
mark@thoburnillustrations.com
www.markthoburn.com

Twitter: @toeburn
Facebook.com: /thoburnillustrations

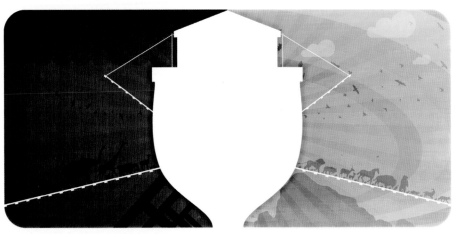

ANDREW HOPGOOD T: 613 9874 2144 M: 0417 319 990
E: andrew@hopgoodillustration.com.au www.hopgoodillustration.com.au

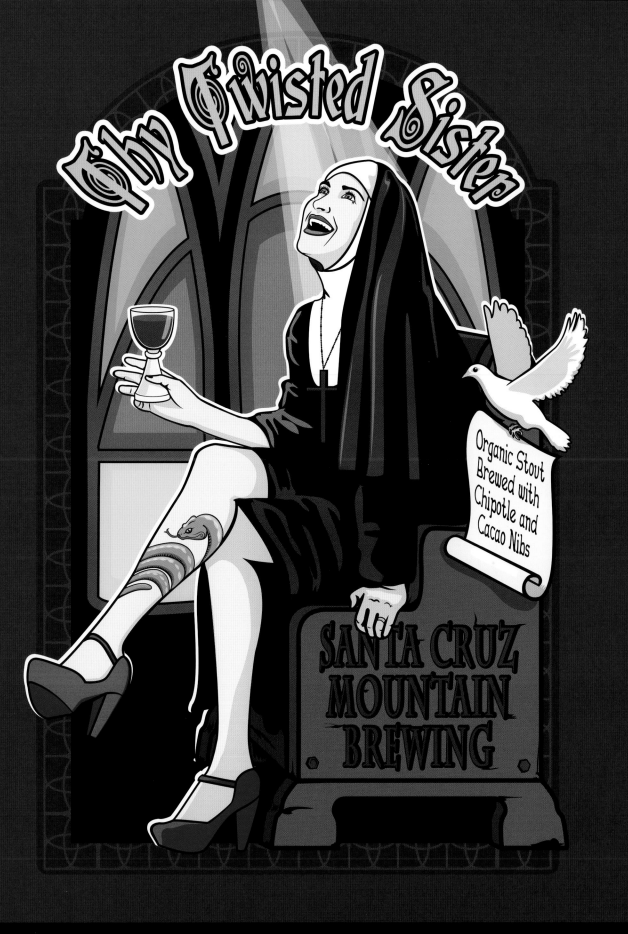

Thy Twisted Sister

Organic Stout Brewed with Chipotle and Cacao Nibs

SANTA CRUZ MOUNTAIN BREWING

Janet Allinger

Illustration & Graphic Design

www.janetallinger.com

831-325-9567

janetallinger@janetallinger.com

Maria Rabinky

Costa Rica

WILL
DRAW
FOR FOOD

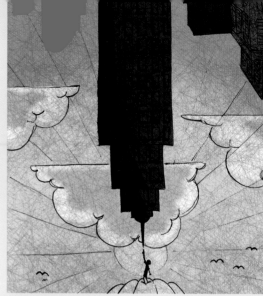

illustration

branding

graphic design

Daniel Chaffin
illustration

chaffinmail@gmail.com | 910.477.0461
www.chaffinillustration.com

MICHAEL ROSS
Graphics

www.mrossgraphics.com / (504) 201-4566 / mlross@cox.net

LAURA S BAILEY

WWW.LAURASBAILEY.COM creative problem solving through painterly illustration
laura@laurasbailey.com phone 314|623|5624

TINMAN  creative

Illustration & Animation by Brett Jubinville

brett@tinman.tv
416.567.2673
Toronto, ON Canada

www.tinman.tv

davewheeler.com   dave@davewheeler.com | 206-854-7017

619.463.4562   pattonbros.com   pattonbros@cox.net

patton brothers
illustration & design, inc.

Greg Ruhl

gregruhl.com

gregruhl@mac.com

416 928 1997

www.tykang.com **TSUNG YANG KANG** *tsungyangkang@gmail.com*

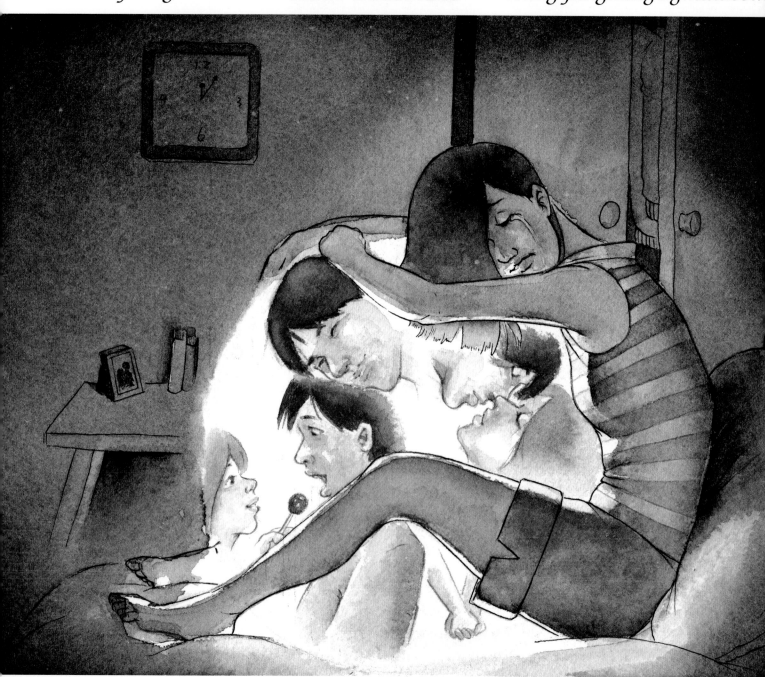

RICHARD THOMPSON *ILLUSTRATION*

Visual problem solving, digital image creation and photo retouching services. I use Photoshop, 3D software and digital photography to create images for billboards, posters, transit shelters, point of purchase, packaging, magazine, corporate collateral, direct mail and anything else you can think of. With almost 20 years experience, my specialty is short deadlines ;-) Visit my website to request a free printed portfolio, to see over 100 images and check out the section on how it's all done:

WWW.RTILLUSTRATION.COM

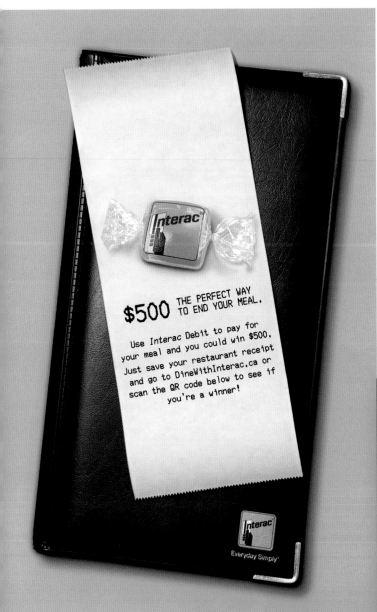

E-MAIL: RICK@RTILLUSTRATION.COM   PHONE: 1-905-425-0093 CELL: 1-905-718-9633

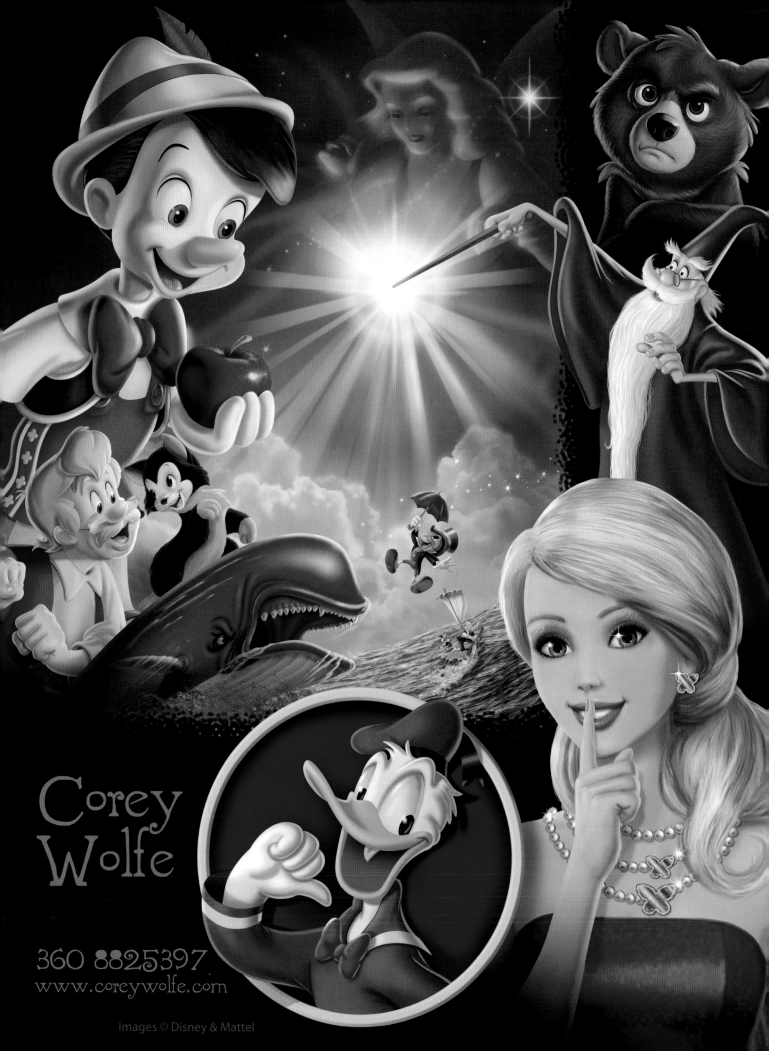

Corey
Wolfe

360 8825397
www.coreywolfe.com

Images © Disney & Mattel

John**Stuart**
Illustrations

www.johnystuart.com

Email
John@johnystuart.com
Phone
905 607 9898

Cafe

No Pets
No Earthlings

Michelle Barbera
tel: 877.787.9896

www.barberaillustration.com
michelle@barberaillustration.com

POP

www.SayoStudio.com

NICOLLE RAGER FULLER
info@SayoStudio.com
425-615-6176

CONCEPTUAL

NATURE

TECHNOLOGY

SCIENCE

MEDICAL

EDITORIAL

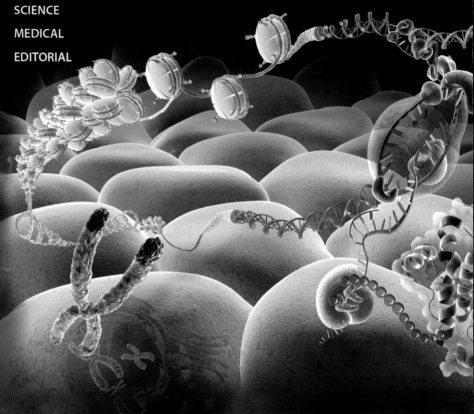

KATE TAYLOR

ILLUSTRATOR

E: kate@yorkshiregirl.freeserve.co.uk

T: 44 (0) 1274 676870

www.ktillustration.co.uk

What you want in life is sometimes just out of reach.......

There is no I in TEAM

A second date was becoming increasingly unlikely......

Another day at work would be one too many..........

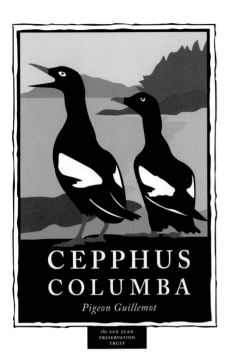

CEPPHUS COLUMBA
Pigeon Guillemot

the SAN JUAN
PRESERVATION
TRUST

THE SAN JUAN PRESERVATION TRUST

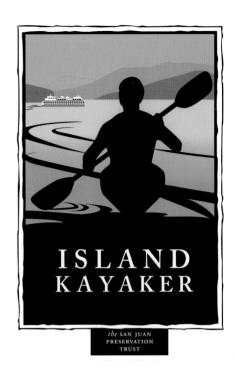

ISLAND KAYAKER

the SAN JUAN
PRESERVATION
TRUST

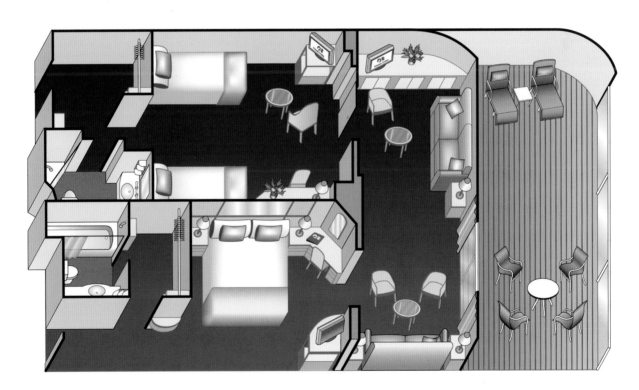

Dusty Deyo Illustration

web: www.dustydeyo.com   email: dustydeyo@ca.rr.com
phone: (310) 398-2699

Glenn Gustafson

G2 ILLUSTRATIONS, INC.

Glenn Gustafson

G2 ILLUSTRATIONS, INC.

 www.glenngustafson.com ■ ggustafson2@yahoo.com ■ 630.947.2785

Moira Fain

www.moirafain.com

I show him how to make a pool in his mashed potatoes.

HISSY FIT

860-712-9192
moirafain@gmail.com

ART GLAZER
2 James Road
Mt. Kisco, NY 10549
TEL: (914) 666-4554
ajglazer@optonline.net

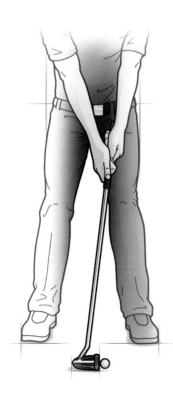

LIFENET® RS Receiving Station

LIFEPAK CR® Plus Defibrillator

LIFEPAK® 12 Defibrillator/Monitor

the MODERN artist

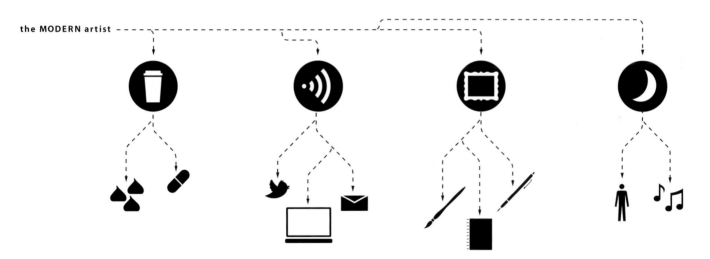

Key Moments in the History of Southwest Airlines

client: **Self-Promo**

TOPDOG™
ILLUSTRATION

www.louisegardner.com

louise@louisegardner.com + 44 (0) 1823 335580

Alaiyo Bradshaw
917 733 0469
alaiyobradshaw.com

Clients include: Amsterdam News, Harcourt Brace, McGraw Hill, PSE&G, New York Times, 20/20

Derek
HUNTER!
illustration/storytelling
www.pirateclub.com
derek@pirateclub.com
801·836·4090

TOMWALLISILLUSTRATION.COM

PAUL BONANNO
ILLUSTRATOR

DECISIVE, COOL, INTELLIGENT... HE'S NONE OF THESE... HE'S

NUKE BLASTEM
GALAXY RANGER

COMIC BOOK

IDRAWPROCARTOONS.COM
IDRAWPROART.COM

"SHERLOCK FLINTSTONE"
FRUITY PEBBLES CONCEPT ART

THE PARANORMALS
by Paul Bonanno

WHAT'S THIS?

COMIC STRIP

CHARACTER DESIGN

PAUL@IDRAWPROART.COM

CHARACTER DESIGN FOR CAPITAL ONE BANK

CARTOONS, CHARACTER DESIGN, COMIC STRIPS, SUPER HEROS, CONCEPT ART, STORYBOARDS, LICENSED CHARACTERS

(908)755-3628

"CRAYON CAPERS"
HARDEES RESTAURANT PROMOTION

djgooddesign.com

DAVID J GOODWIN • ILLUSTRATOR / DESIGNER 909 579 9730

+1 617.877.1899   krishna@nanuillustration.com   www.nanuillustration.com

NANU ILLUSTRATION

Darren McKee Illustration

214-343-8766

mckeeldarren@hotmail.com

Darren McKee   •   (214) 343-8766   •   mckeeldarren@hotmail.com

Sarah Wisbey

www.WISBEYDESIGN.com   585.244.7176

Email: pmcdarby@earthlink.net

Phone: 203-257-2772

PROPERTY OF MLS. Designed by Richard Levy and Patrick McDarby

PROPERTY OF UFL. designed by PurePartner Designs' Ron Caruso and Patrick McDarby

PROPERTY OF GOOD HUMOR. Vector illustration for Cuticone Design

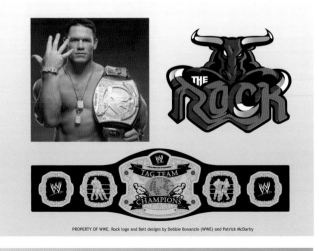
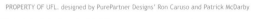

PROPERTY OF WWE. Rock logo and Belt designs by Debbie Bonanzio (WWE) and Patrick McDarby

www.pyramyddesigns.com

415

Maghen Brown
Illustrator

www.maghenbrown.com   914-466-5936   Maghen@aol.com

Antony Hare, Private Illustrator
ahpi.ca   226-688-6082

WWW.JESSICAPALMERART.BIZ   JESS@JESSICAPALMER.BIZ   0044 7701 024530

Jeffrey B. McKeever

illustration   fantasy   sci-fi   social   commentary

908-859-5812   screamingcelt@verizon.net   screamingceltstudio.com

OLYMPIC PENINSULA
WASHINGTON STATE · The DEPARTMENT of DEPENDABILITY

With a DD15, it's just a walk in the park.
CONTINENTAL DIVIDE
LOVELAND PASS, COLO · The DEPARTMENT of MASSIVE TORQUE

240,000 metric tonnes of gold, silver and copper mined each day.
GRASBERG MINE
PUNCAK JAYA, INDONESIA · The DEPARTMENT of MOVING MOUNTAINS

STUART HIGHWAY
NORTHERN TERRITORY **AUSTRALIA** · The DEPARTMENT of NEVER QUITS

Power, durability and a never-say-die attitude.
HOOVER DAM BYPASS
ARIZONA · NEVADA · The DEPARTMENT of BRUTE FORCE

WIND ENERGY CENTER
IOWA, USA · The DEPARTMENT of WIDE OPEN SPACES

Moving a highway underground takes a real work truck.
THE BIG DIG
BOSTON, MASSACHUSETTS · The DEPARTMENT of WICKED TOUGH

PERMIAN BASIN
ODESSA, TEXAS · The DEPARTMENT of NO EXCUSES

To survive this town, it has to be tough.
MOTOR CITY
DETROIT, MICHIGAN · The DEPARTMENT of SMOOTH RIDES

Incredible performance, no matter what the conditions.
SEA-TO-SKY HIGHWAY
WHISTLER, BC · The DEPARTMENT of GETTING IT DONE

ALBERTA TAR SANDS
ALBERTA, CANADA · The DEPARTMENT of NO CRYBABIES

HARBOURFRONT CENTRE
TORONTO, ONTARIO · The DEPARTMENT of WHATEVER IT TAKES

JEFF FOSTER.com

LEGENDS OF THE NORTHWOODS

Calendar
503 320 1207
Portland OR

ALAN GREENSPAN

CRAIG MCGILL

A cool mud bath is nice at the end of a hot day.

Betsy Wallin
betsywallin@gmail.com
www.betsywallin.com
33 6 59 87 53 49
(France)

Goodnight, chickens.
See you in the morning.

STUDIO FORONDA

e: anthonyforonda@me.com

w: www.studioforonda.com

p: 301.538.2344

anthony foronda

wesleybedrosian.com

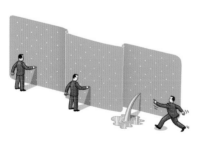

Wesley Bedrosian | Illustration | 100 Montclair Ave | Montclair, NJ 07042 | 973.233.0093 | mail@wesleybedrosian.com

Clients include: The New York Times, Barron's, Vanity Fair, Business Week, Billboard Magazine, Fortune, The Wall Street Journal, The Progressive, Time, Harvard Medical, Forbes, The Boston Globe, The Washington Post, New York Magazine, SmartMoney, The Nation.

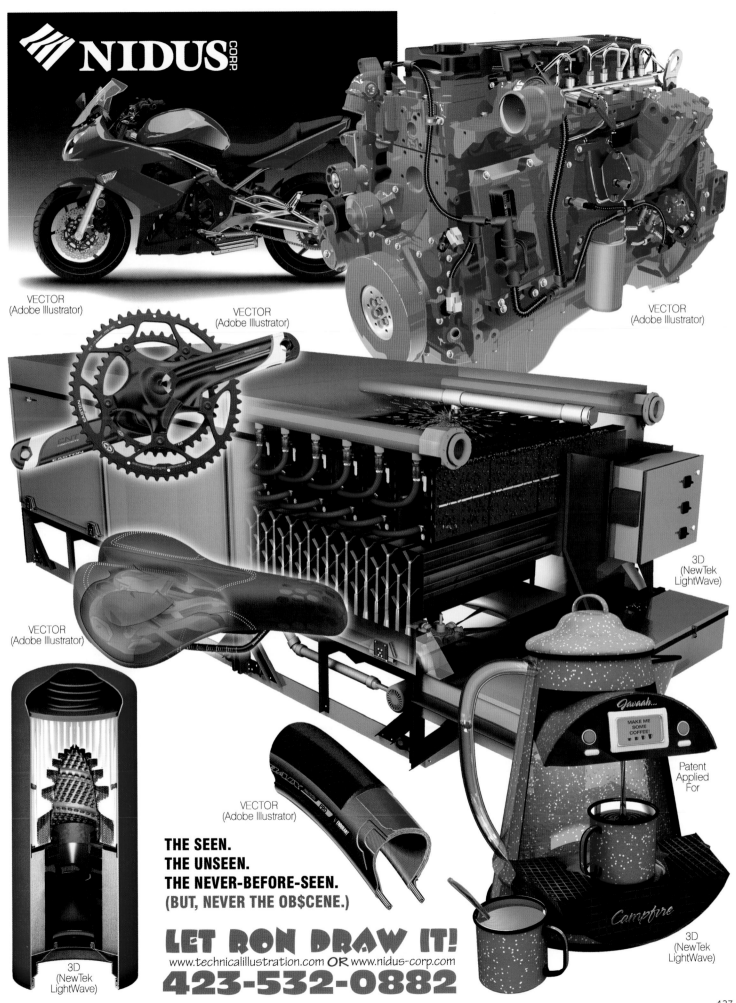

427

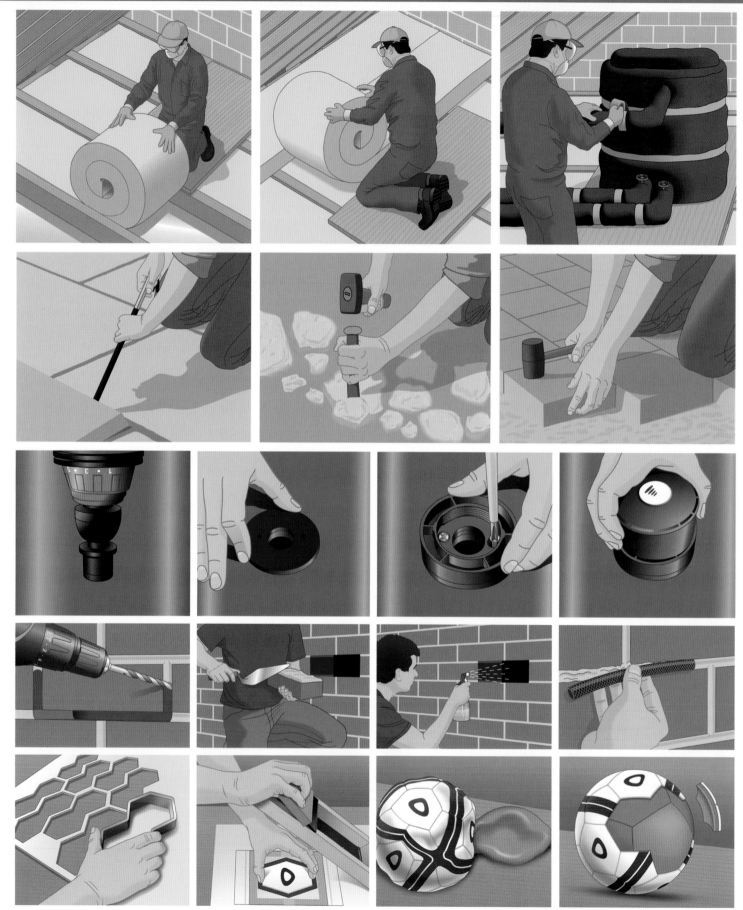

428

This is Toby.

This is Carla.

That is Bartholomew and Linda, Jasper, Chad, Jill, Anita, Nobu, and Robin.

That is Josephine.

This is Mr. Melvin McMeowster.

That is Ralph and Rufus. Oh, sorry. It's Rufus and Ralph.

This is Mrs. Margaret Maria Maria Lebandowski Nascimento dama de Oliveira Blumenfeld Oliseh Hashemian Smith. She was married many times.

And that's me, and I'm off to lunch.

MISA SABURI

misasaburi.com
617.834.8511
saburi.misa@gmail.com

I want to say hi, but I'm too shy

MAPS BY MATHISON

Hovel

Cart Track

CHANNEL

GUILDER

FLORIN

Oak Tree

Ambush

Rope

Duel

Cliffs of Insanity

Picnic

Ravine

Kidnappers' Ship

Fire Swamp

Snow Sand

Pursuit Ship

Cove

Bursts of Flame

Zoo of Death

The *Revenge*

Wheelbarrow

The Armada

R.O.U.S.

Castle

Giant Eel Bay

Florin City
Great Square

Fishing Village

Fezzik's Cave

Thieves' Quarter

CHANNEL of GUILDER

Miracle Max's Hut

Falkbridge's Alehouse

N E S W

The Princess Bride, by William Goldman

The Unnameables, by Ellen Booraem

TOWN

N W E S

TANNERY

SAWYER-TANNER

WEAVER SHOP

TAILOR SHOP

COBBLER SHOP

NORTH SHORE ROAD

PICKLER

FORGE

COOK'S

CARVER SHOP

MERCHANTS ROAD

MAIN STREET

BOG ROAD

MILL STREAM

GRIST MILL

OVEN HOUSE

CARVER HOUSE

GLAZER SHOP

TOWN HALL

FARMER-GARDENER

SOUTH SHORE ROAD

CARTWRIGHT SHOP

POTTER-CARPENTER

BAITSHED LANE

WHARF

WATERMAN'S ROAD

HARBOR LANE

POINT ROAD

HARBORSIDE

POTTERY

FISHERS LANE

Jeff Mathison
jcmaps@mac.com or jcmaps6@gmail.com
www.mapsbymathison.com
www.directoryofillustration.com/ArtistPortfolioThumbs.aspx?AID=6290
Contact me for any kind of illustrative map, simple or complex. Birdseye views are my specialty.

430

ZERO POINT POWER 3D
ILLUSTRATION·ANIMATION

www.scottpadbury.com
704-545-4588
zeropointpower3d@gmail.com

"Zombie Kings" Winner Best Short Film Disney Indie Fest

State Aunthentics, Shoe Design Concept 3D

Ingersoll Rand 3d Modeling, Brochure and Website Illustrations

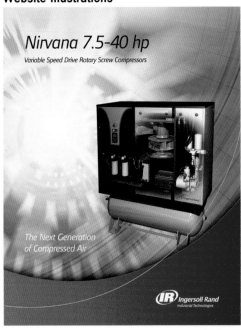

Nirvana 7.5-40 hp
Variable Speed Drive Rotary Screw Compressors

The Next Generation
of Compressed Air

Ingersoll Rand
Industrial Technologies

Integrated Variable Speed Drive...

VSD Controlled Capacity Regulation

Responding to fluctuation in your system demand and maintaining a close controlled system pressure, Nirvana automatically adjusts its compressed air output to achieve the highest efficiency for your operation.

This avoids wasted energy caused by excessive pressure band or unloaded running, allowing you to:

· Achieve higher productivity from your air system
· Maintain optimum performance from the equipment you operate
· Save up to 35% energy cost

American Wick Drain, Product Illustrations Usage

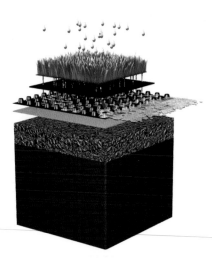

Denise Clemmensen illustration

deniseclem@verizon.net • www.deniseclemmensen.com • (818) 893-3298

Diana Lisanto

dianalisanto.com illustration drlisanto@gmail.com

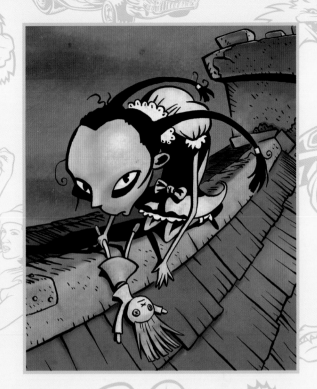

CHUCK REGAN

I draw that weird stuff.

RAYGUNS AND MAYHEM.COM

cdr@cdregan.com

Adam Schechter   201 230 4541   www.adamschechter.com

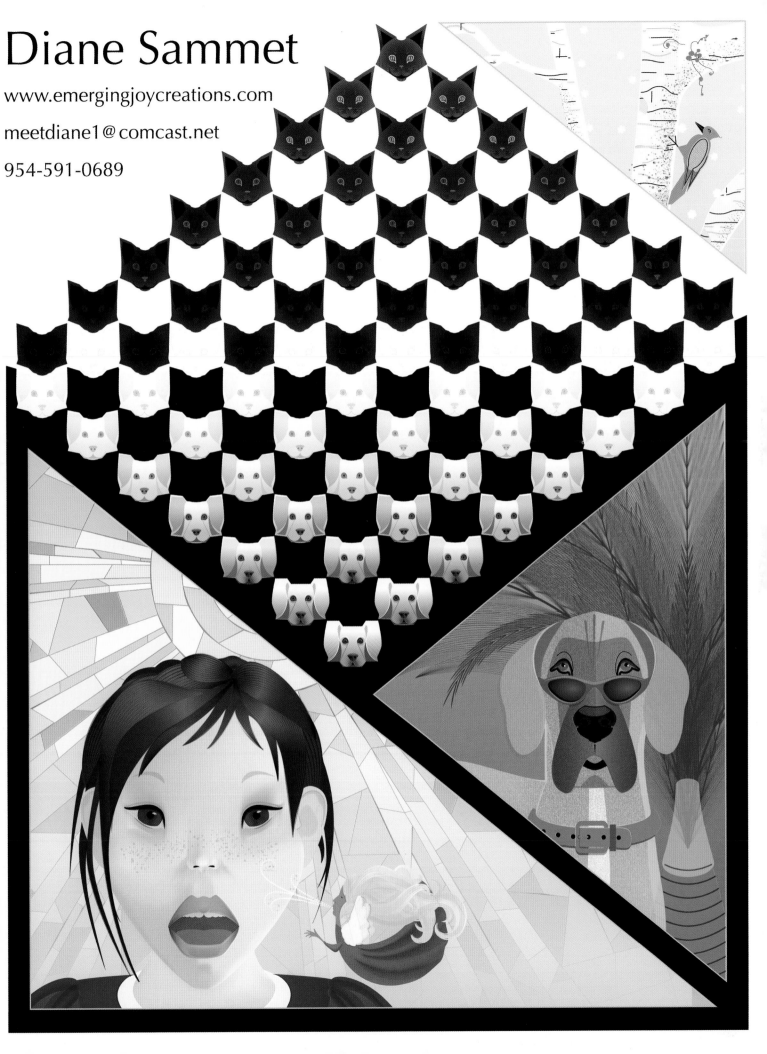

Diane Sammet

www.emergingjoycreations.com

meetdiane1@comcast.net

954-591-0689

Illustration · Animation · Design

The Learning Journey

Stephen Traino

440

barbara kelley

631.754.7374 | www.barbarakelley.com | artarch@optonline.net

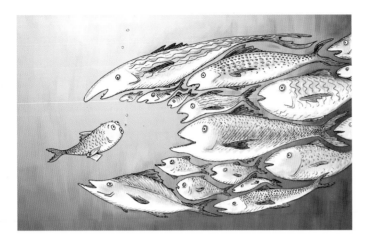

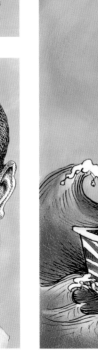

Clients from this page: The Wall Street Journal, The Hoover Institute Defining Ideas

laura
guill
ILLUSTRATION

lauraguill.com ✂ laura@lauraguill.com

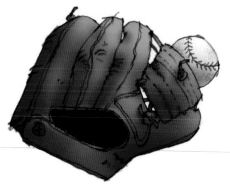

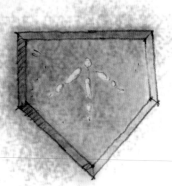

TAIA MORLEY

651.436.8855
taia@taiamorley.com

David Lyttleton   www.davidlyttleton.com   david.lyttleton@virgin.net   davidlyttleton33@gmail.com   +44(0)1782 613564   07958 421092

Traci Bixby
Illustration

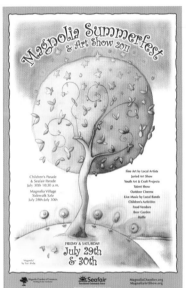

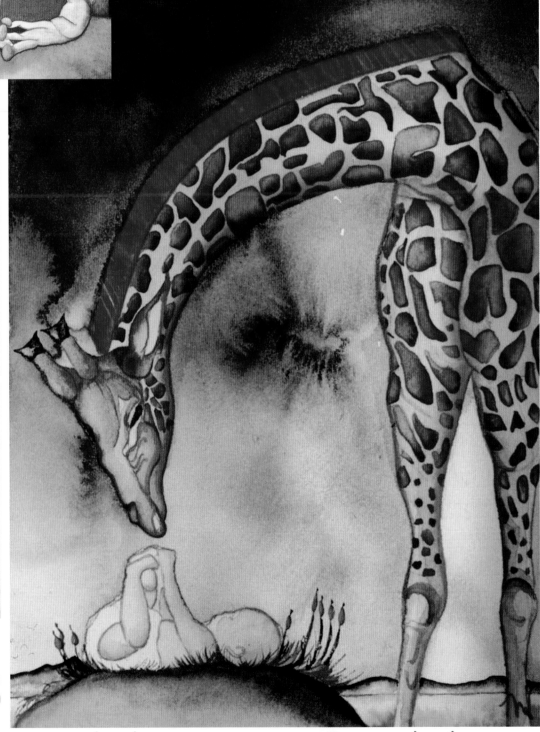

206-605-7984

tracibixby.com   traci@tracibixby.com

Children's Illustration   Fantasy   Hyper-Realism

Cathy Rowe

916.300.9607

www.cathyrowe.com

cathyrowe.art@gmail.com

461

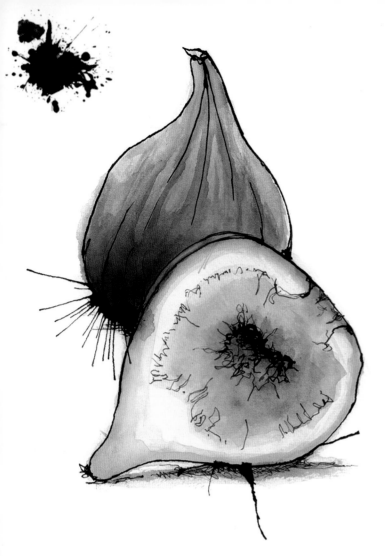

Rob Cowan

illustration

Rob Cowan   +61 434 008549   info@robcowan.com.au   www.robcowan.com.au

annemarieperks

www.annemarieperks.com ~ justanillustrator@me.com ~ +44 1494 775416

Patrick Welsh – Illustration

ELIZABETH WHELAN

elizabethwhelanillustrator.com   508.560.0083

Daniel Rubinstein
www.danielrubinstein.com

dj@danielrubinstein.com

407-619-3142

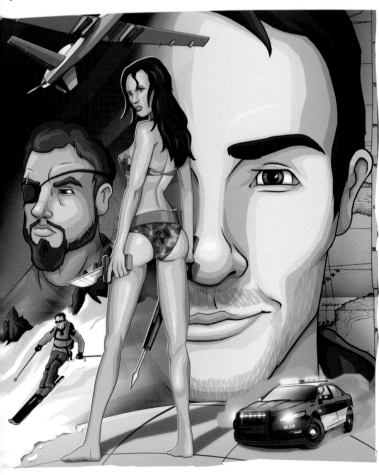

CHARLIE GRIAK

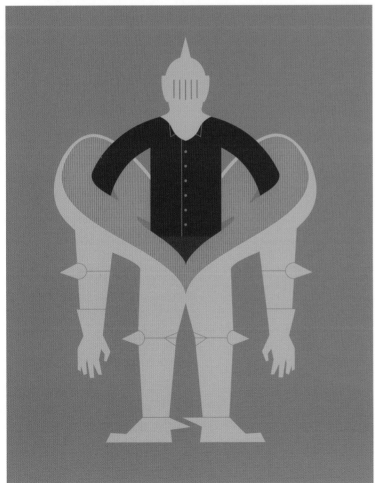
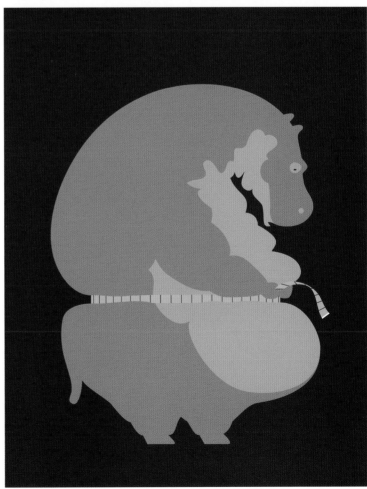

Aad Goudappel Illustrations | aad@aadgoudappel.com | +31 (0)10 414 74 93 | www.aadgoudappel.com

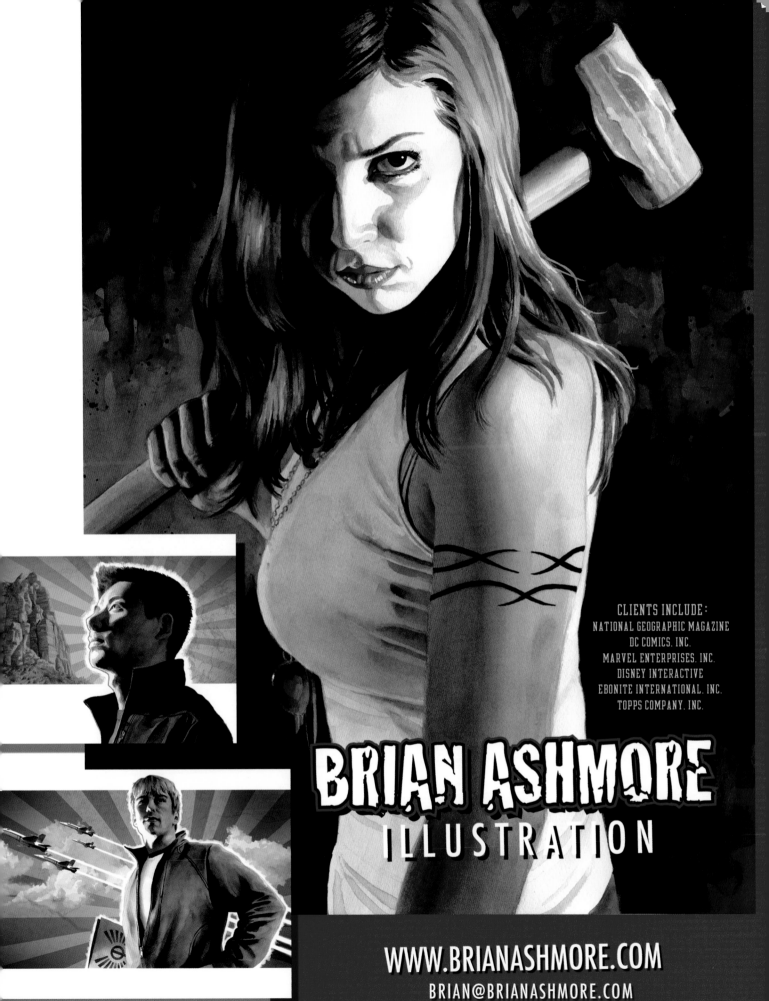

noble

www.noblepaints.com
artbrush9@yahoo.com

Mark Hess
914.232.5870
Mark@HessDesignWorks.com

RON DUNN
310.427.5409
potosiboy@yahoo.com | www.rondunnart.com

LONDON

Matt Oxborrow illustration

www.mattoxborrow.co.uk | +44 (0)7952 539269

matt@mattoxborrow.co.uk

Tim Grajek
illustration

914.332.9704 💬 timgrajek@aol.com 🖱 www.timgrajek.com

Margaret Fox & Tim Grajek Photo/Illustration Partners

"The First Dog" by Benjamin Cheever

Steven Quentin: www.gizmoart.net   gizmoart12@gmail.com   214-507-5363

J.R.R. TOLKIEN

NOT ALL THOSE WHO WANDER ARE LOST

SIGNORINA *Navarra*
DESIGN & HAND-LETTERING

> signorinanavarra.com > 201.406.9837
> info@signorinanavarra.com

R.S. Posnak
www.rsposnak.com
rs@rsposnak.com
707-364-8321

483

FUN-1

Illustration & Design Studio

P.O. Box 21194, Columbus, OH 43221
614.326.3861 • fun-1studio.com
Jan Benham, Illustrator

Orla Roche

studio@orlaroche.com +353 86 3978650

JOHN ROWE

PET THIEF STUDIO
www.john-rowe.com

JOHN@JOHN-ROWE.COM 818-249-2330

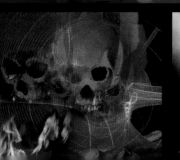

Walt Disney
YOUNG
BLACK STALLION
EXCLUSIVELY IN IMAX™ THEATRES
TICKETS ON SALE NOW! CALL 1-888-DISNEY6

DUNGEONS & DRAGONS

Endangered Species   39c

United Nations

Illustration & Design

Levinity

Levene Wong
levenewong.com
levinity@gmail.com

 THE **BLUE GRIFFIN**

EDITORIAL • FANTASY • SCI-FI • COMIC • POP • CONCEPTUAL
WWW.THEBLUEGRIFFIN.COM   INFO@THEBLUEGRIFFIN.COM   718-305-1205

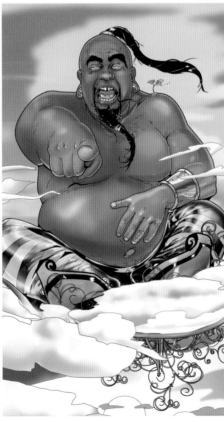

THE **BLUE GRIFFIN**

EDITORIAL • FANTASY • SCI-FI • COMIC • POP • CONCEPTUAL

WWW.THEBLUEGRIFFIN.COM   INFO@THEBLUEGRIFFIN.COM   718-305-1205

www.GregPaprocki.com
Greg@GregPaprocki.com
1(402) 932-0722

GREG PAPROCKI

all artwork property of © Greg Paprocki 2012

SWEET SMELL OF VICTORY
ZOMBIE OPS
Official Paranormal Squad

CALVIN
NICHOLLS

PAPER SCULPTURE

CALVIN@CALVINNICHOLLS.COM - 705-878-1640

JOSHUA J STEWART

ILLUSTRATION & CONCEPT ART

208.940.2303

josh@joshuajstewart.com

WWW.JOSHUAJSTEWART.COM

Fran
Gregory

Illustration | Graphic Design
frangregoryart.com
1.708.484.7201

David Holmes

5 Calvert Street, Primrose Hill, London UK NW1 8NE
david@cecilholmes.demon.co.uk
www.davidcecilholmes.com

goopymart

cartoon art & design

Contact: Will Guy

415.290.3016

goopymart.com

goopymart@gmail.com

EDGAR STEWART

p: 978.318.0004
e: edgar@edgarstewart.net
edgarstewart.com

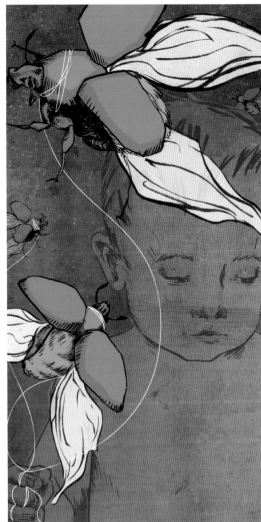

SACHA PENN

ILLUSTRATOR
GRAPHIC DESIGNER

SACHA@SACHAILLUSTRATES.COM
714/262.6781

Agent Illustrateur

www.agentillustrateur.com
info@agentillustrateur.com

Nicole Allin
206•906•9147
allinart@fastmail.fm   www.allinart.net

CHRISTOPHER ALLAN

chris@cjksallan.com
267-218-5787

see more of
my work at
www.cjksallan.com

504

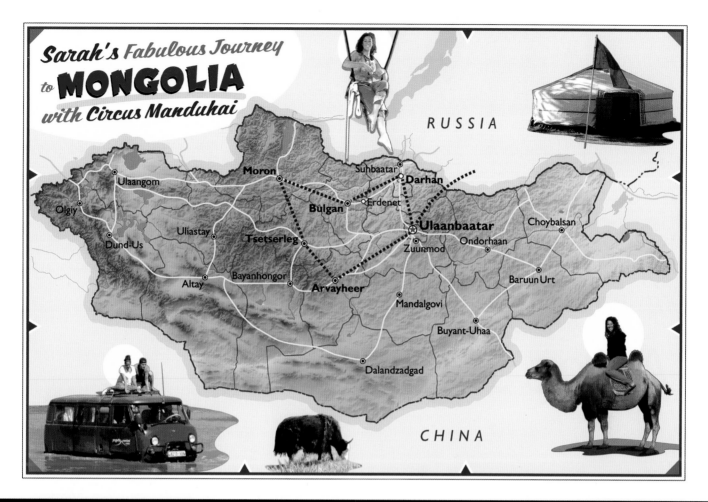

Sarah's Fabulous Journey to MONGOLIA with Circus Manduhai

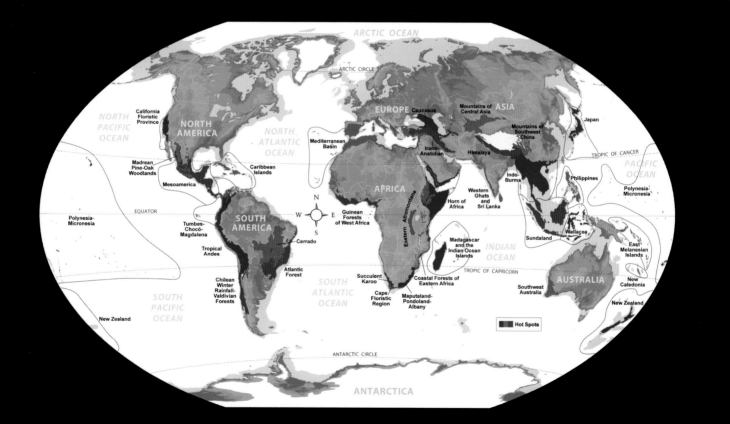

505

Notre Dame Magazine, Summer 2011, "The Way We Were" spot & full page

Alice Flynn

Books . Editorial . Publishing . Illustration

aliceflynn.com   alice@aliceflynn.com   406.209.6779

"Camp Of The Angel" young reader book jacket

James L. Barry
illustration · comics · animation
www.JLBarry.com
917-297-0483

Little Miss Muffett sat on a tuffet...

Eating her curds and whey.

Along came a Spider...

And sat down beside her.

PSSH

So she shot him with bugspray!

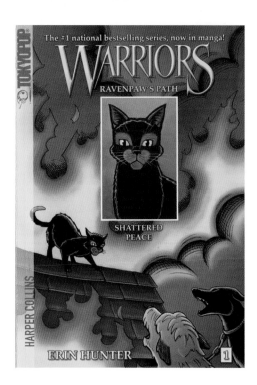

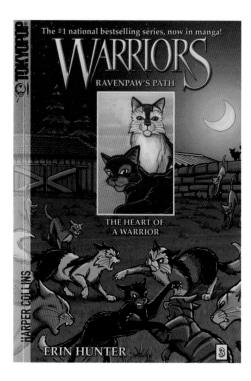

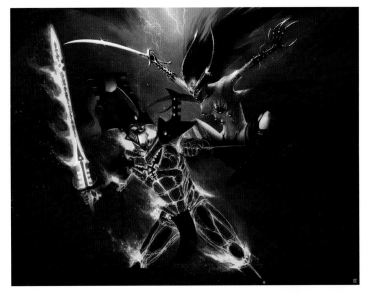

NICHOLAS KAY
FREELANCE ARTIST + ILLUSTRATOR

www.nicholaskay.com
artist@nicholaskay.com

Blog: www.http://nicholaskay.blogspot.com/
Facebook Page: Nicholas Kay
Twitter: @nicholasmkay
DeviantArt: Klausmasterflex
YouTube Channel: Klausmasterflex

Albert Campbell | Illustrator | 949.887.1419 | albertcdesign.com | ac@albertcdesign.com

www.stephenburdickdesign.com

Graphic design and illustration for print and online media. Clients include WGBH, Eastern Bank, Physicans for Social Responsibility, Nantucket Wine Festival, Nantucket Comedy Festival. Seen in the *Boston Globe, Utne Magazine, Bay Windows, Print Magazine, Applied Arts,* and *Graphic Design USA.* Follow our blog at sbdesign.posterous.com.

20 Piedmont Street
Boston, MA 02116
phone: (617) 695-1400
toll free: 877-SBD-4ART (723-4278)
email: sbdesign@shore.net
www.stephenburdickdesign.com

stephen
burdick
design

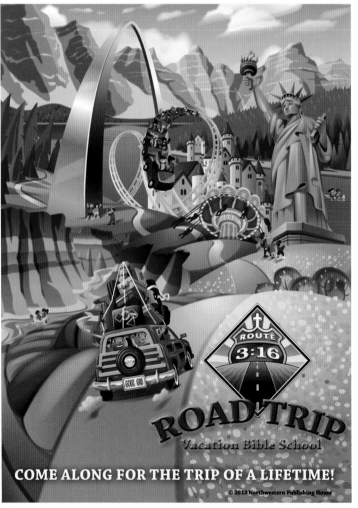

CHRISTINE MACTERNAN
WWW.CRMACTERNAN.COM
CMACTERNAN@GMAIL.COM

www.mariasantiago.com
416.576.2742

515

Michaela Eaves

+1 425.753.6709 | michaela@michaelaeaves.com

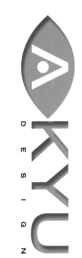

Adam Questell (questell@akyudesign.com)
9911 Vogue Lane Houston, TX 77080
713.468.9595 (tel) 713.392.3628 (cel)
w w w . a k y u d e s i g n . c o m

3D graphics should do more than inform. They should illuminate.

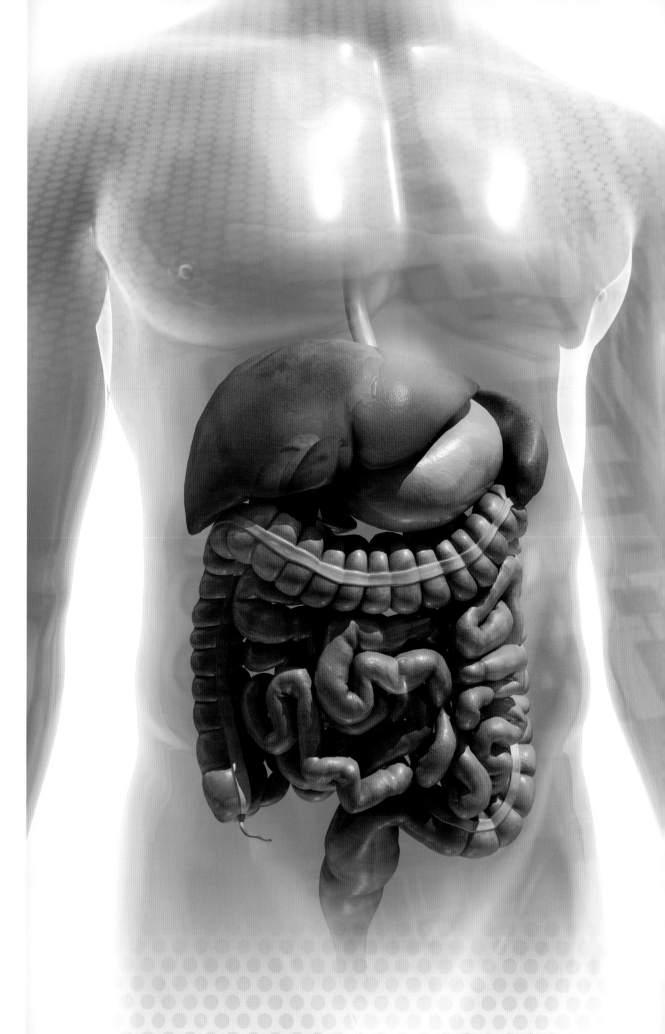

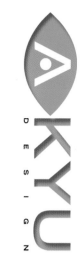

Lesley Wolf

Illustration W *Design*

lesley@wolfdesign.net • www.lesleywolf.com • www.wolfdesign.net • 805.962.6621

jenean@jeneanmorrison.com
901.336.5705

Jenean Morrison
surface design and illustration

www.jeneanmorrison.com

ian vanderhill

digital illustration

ianvanderhill.com   616.510.6888
ianvanderhill@gmail.com

DREW MORRISON

BROOKLYN, NEW YORK

Steve Björkman

949-349-0109   Stevebjorkman.com   stevebjorkman@sbcglobal.net

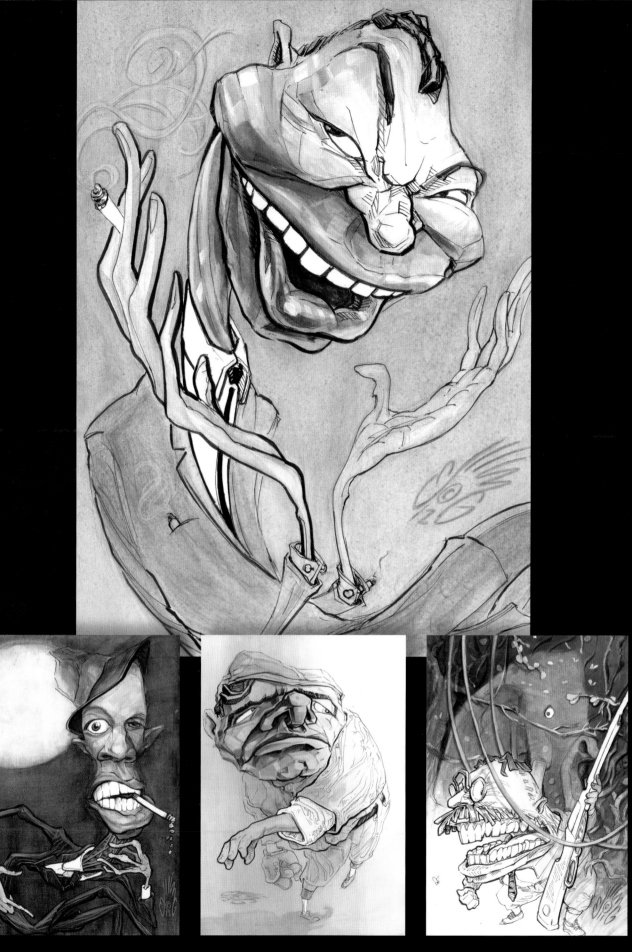

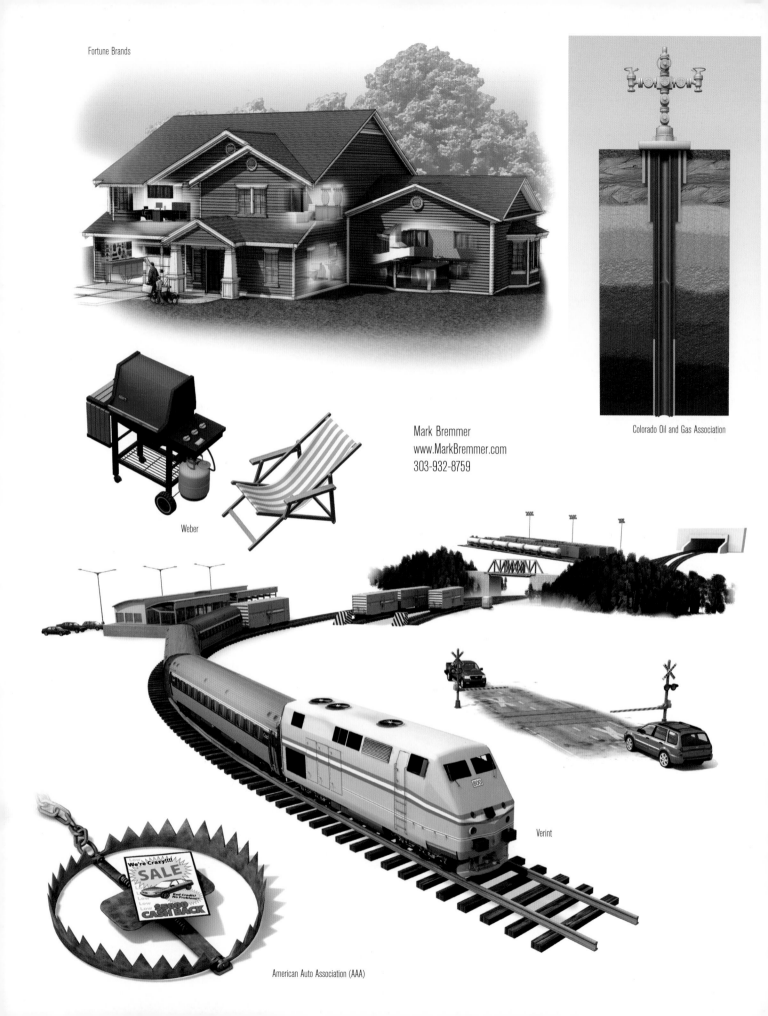

Fortune Brands

Colorado Oil and Gas Association

Mark Bremmer
www.MarkBremmer.com
303-932-8759

Weber

Verint

American Auto Association (AAA)

MATT MALEY

CARTOON ★ ILLUSTRATION ★ DESIGN

WWW.VISUALSTUFFSTUDIOS.COM ★ VISUALSTUFF@EARTHLINK.NET ★ (914)466-9761

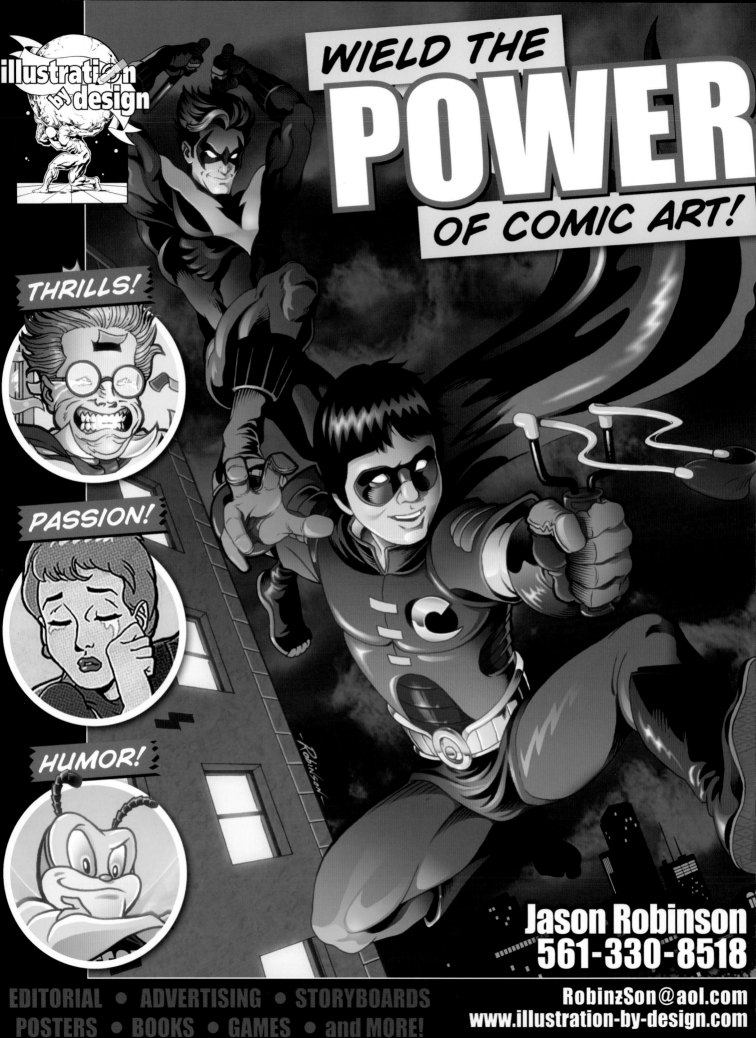

full0.com
416 939 4298
gball@full0.com

vis dev
interactive
ip dev

Gavin Ball
FULL CIRCLE CS inc.

FULL CIRCLE

▼ For *Newsweek* magazine

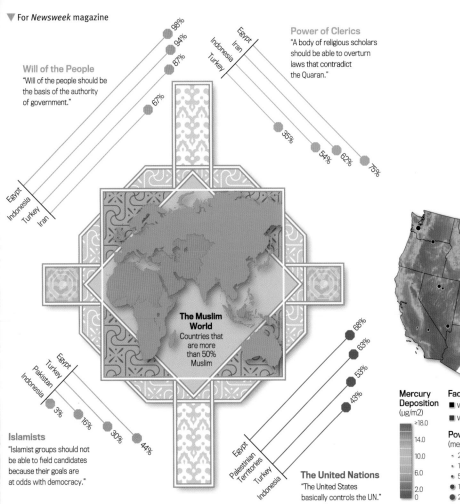

Will of the People
"Will of the people should be the basis of the authority of government."

98%
94%
87%

67%

Egypt
Indonesia
Turkey
Iran

Power of Clerics
"A body of religious scholars should be able to overturn laws that contradict the Quaran."

Egypt
Iran
Indonesia
Turkey

35%
54%
62%
75%

The Muslim World
Countries that are more than 50% Muslim

Islamists
"Islamist groups should not be able to field candidates because their goals are at odds with democracy."

Egypt
Turkey
Pakistan
Indonesia

3%
16%
30%
44%

68%
63%
53%
43%

Egypt
Palestinian Territories
Turkey
Indonesia

The United Nations
"The United States basically controls the UN."

CAROL ZUBER-MALLISON
214-906-4162
carol@zmgraphics.com
2340 Edwin St.
Fort Worth, Texas 76110-6634

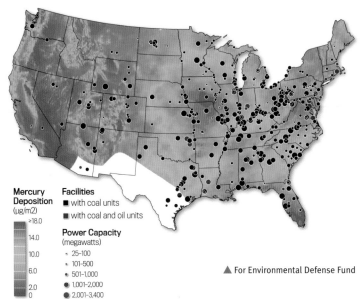

Mercury Deposition (µg/m2)
≥18.0
14.0
10.0
6.0
2.0
0

Facilities
■ with coal units
■ with coal and oil units

Power Capacity (megawatts)
· 25–100
· 101–500
· 501–1,000
● 1,001–2,000
● 2,001–3,400

▲ For Environmental Defense Fund

IN-STORE DISPLAY
DIGITAL MEDIA
Packaging
Direct mail
TV
MEASUREMENT
Promotions
TRADITIONAL MEDIA
Print ads
SOLD

TRADITIONAL
SHOPPER MARKETING

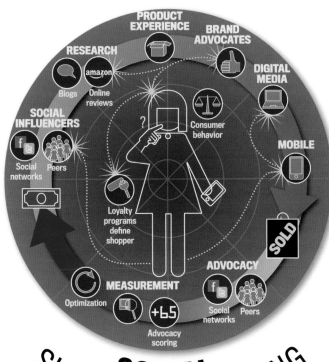

PRODUCT EXPERIENCE
BRAND ADVOCATES
RESEARCH
amazon
DIGITAL MEDIA
Blogs
Online reviews
SOCIAL INFLUENCERS
Consumer behavior
Social networks
Peers
MOBILE
Loyalty programs define shopper
MEASUREMENT
Optimization
+65
Advocacy scoring
ADVOCACY
Social networks
Peers
SOLD

SOCIAL
SHOPPER MARKETING

▲ For BzzAgent

illustrator · benicia, CA · 707-746-1662 · 707-334-3253 · gregg@greggvalley.com · greggvalley.com

llustrator · benicia, CA · 707-746-1662 · 707-334-3253 · gregg@greggvalley.com · greggvalley.com

feuer ᔆᴹ
ILLUSTRATION

art for effective education
in science, medicine and dentistry

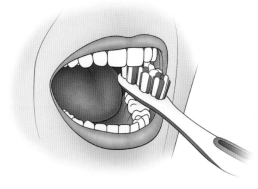

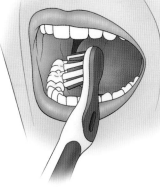

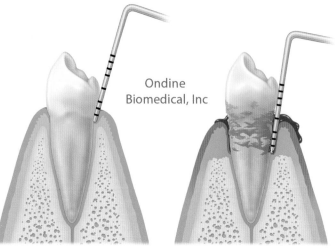

Ondine
Biomedical, Inc

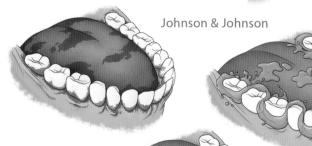

Johnson & Johnson

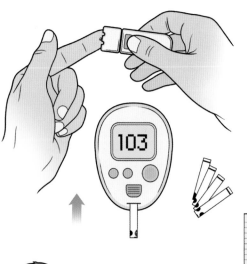

The Hormone
Health Network

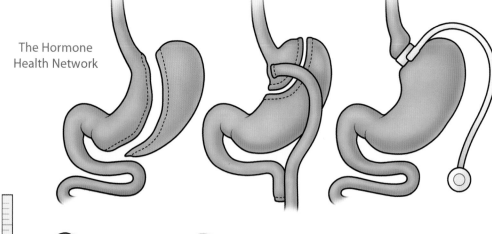

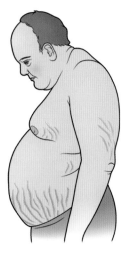

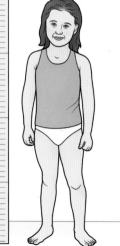

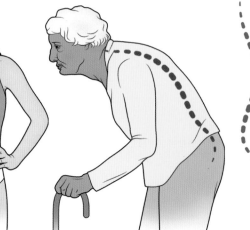

412-353-9278 • molly@feuerillustration.com • www.feuerillustration.com

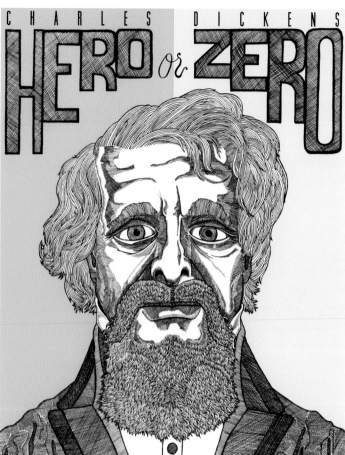

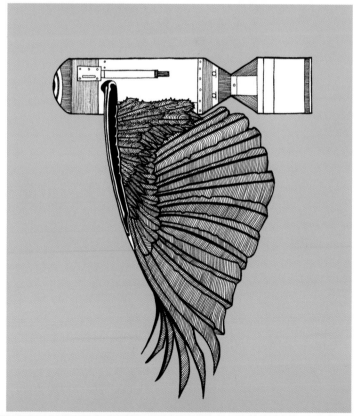

Allison M. Healy   ahealy@ah-creative.com   651.331.6407

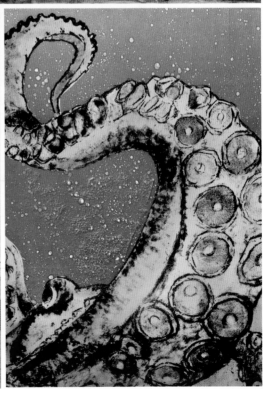

YANA BEYLINSON

Yana Beylinson

www.yanabeylinson.com | ybeylins@gmail.com | 917.319.0413

With services ranging from illustration and book design to website and identity design, Ryan Lanigan can do it all. He would love the opportunity to help with your next project.

RYAN LANIGAN
award-winning design & illustration

606.669.3148 | ryanlanigan.com

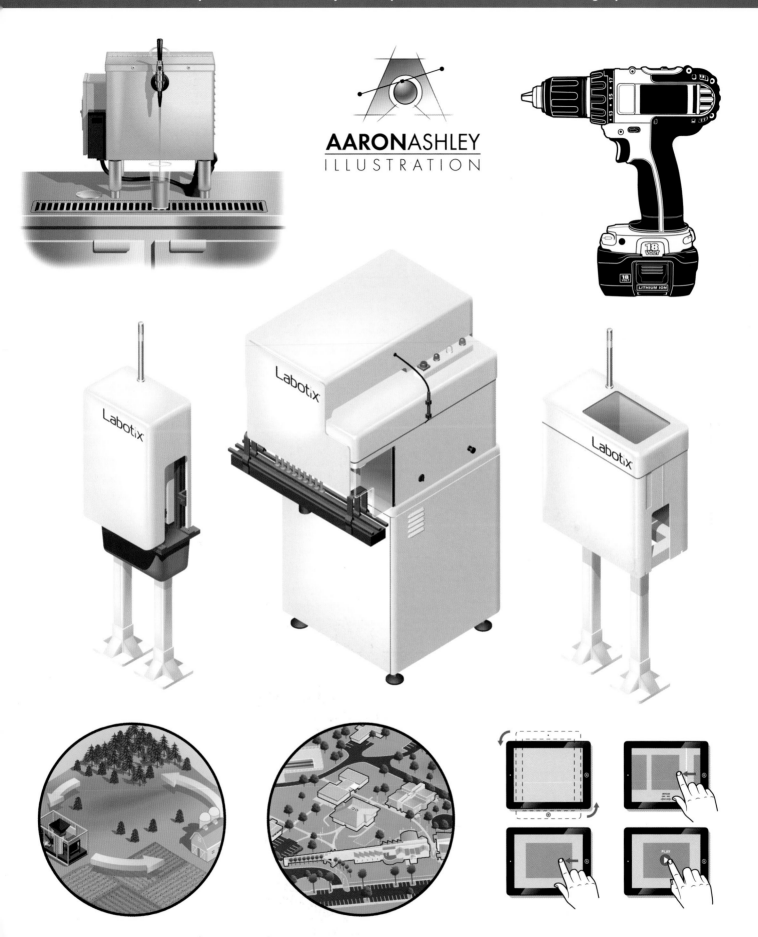

AARONASHLEY
ILLUSTRATION

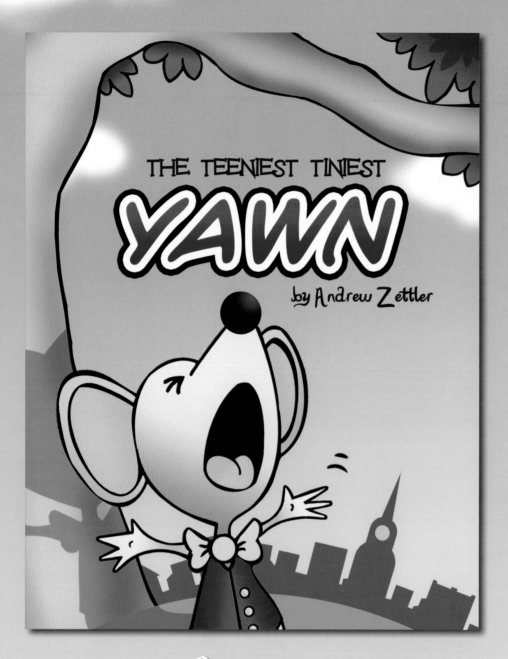

AUTISM & ASPERGERS SUPPORT
Callie Claire For Kids

A MORTGAGE YOU WILL LOVE
A Bank You Can Trust.

Whimsical & Vibrant
Illustration For

Children's Markets • Publishing
Advertising • Packaging
Editorial • Characters

andrew zettler

www.AndrewZettler.com • ADZettler@gmail.com • 1.240.372.1670

Steve Spencer

Contact Information:
spinadelic@aol.com

spinadelic.com

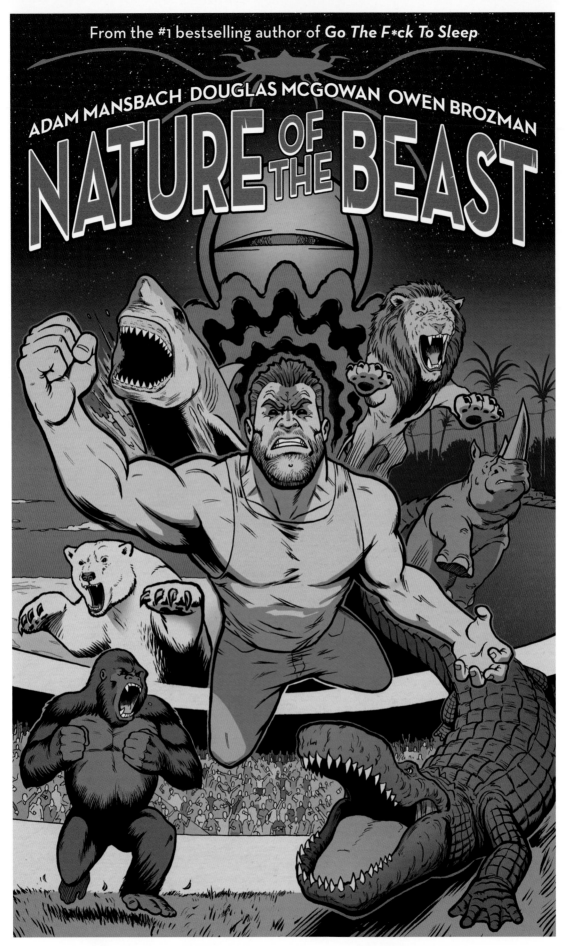

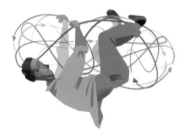

mick wiggins illustration

mickwiggins.com

510-524-3076

mick@mickwiggins.com

SEUSSICAL
THE MUSICAL

Scott J. Fowler
(646) 752-2528
ActingOutDesign.com

GUYS AND DOLLS

A Little Night Music

Rudy-Jan Faber Illustration

THE AMAZING
TATTOOED
★ LADY ★

1923

WWW.RUDYFABER.COM   CONTACT@RUDYFABER.COM   T.+31641832049

KOZ.WOODCUT. 757-253-8950
PAULAGOODMANKOZ.COM
VITABREVE@COX.NET

" TOP DOLLAR"

ELIZABETHHAYWOOD.COM
704 572 0370
81 ORCHARD STREET
NEW YORK, NY
ELIZABETH@ELIZABETHHAYWOOD.COM

Matthew Holmes · Artist
4760 American River Drive
Carmichael, CA 95608

916-971-4727
matthewholmes@att.net

Joan Reilly
illustration@joanreilly.com
109 South 5th Street, #202
Brooklyn, NY 11249
(917) 543-6327

ASHLEY BARRON
ILLUSTRATION

1.905.995.0020 hello@ashleybarron.com
www.ashleybarron.com

Suzy Wear
ILLUSTRATION & ART

CARLA BAUER

WOODCUT ILLUSTRATION

247 WEST 30TH ST

SUITE 10F

NEW YORK NY 10001

t   212 807 8305

f   212 206 8005

c   646 335 5202

e   carlabauer@earthlink.net

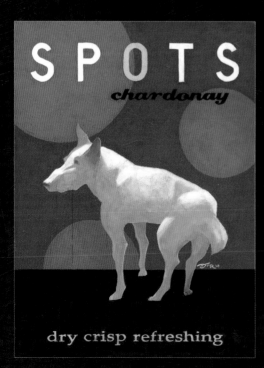

SPOTS
chardonay

dry crisp refreshing

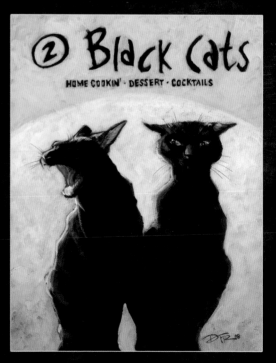

② Black Cats

HOME COOKIN' · DESSERT · COCKTAILS

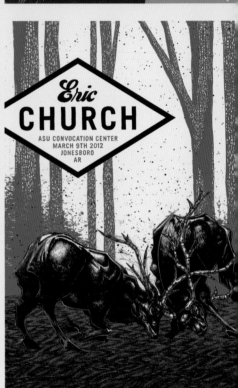

Eric
CHURCH
ASU CONVOCATION CENTER
MARCH 9TH 2012
JONESBORO
AR

JOHN VOGL | THEBUNGALOO.COM | JOHN@THEBUNGALOO.COM

SATURDAY, MAY 28
SF POPFEST PRESENTS
A SLUMBERLAND
RECORDS SHOWCASE

WITH
14 ICED BEARS
PHIL WILSON
NEVEREVER
ART MUSEUMS
DEVON WILLIAMS
BRILLIANT COLORS
TERRY MALTS
SEA LIONS
KIDS ON A CRIME SPREE
ENGLISH SINGLES
PLUS DJ KID FROSTBITE

THE RICKSHAW STOP | 5PM
155 FELL STREET
SAN FRANCISCO

LIVE NATION PRESENTS
LOTUS

Adobe | Illustrator®
Flash®

Daniel Johnson

Digital illustration/matte painting NAPP Guru award winner, 2007
3D models/textures/multimedia Layers Magazine featured designer, 2008
Flash/animation/web design Adobe Certified Instructor (ACI) and Expert (ACE), CS5

707.478.2790 danjohn8@comcast.net www.danjohnsonimagery.com photoshop-illustration.blogspot.com

Kevin Eslinger
ILLUSTRATION

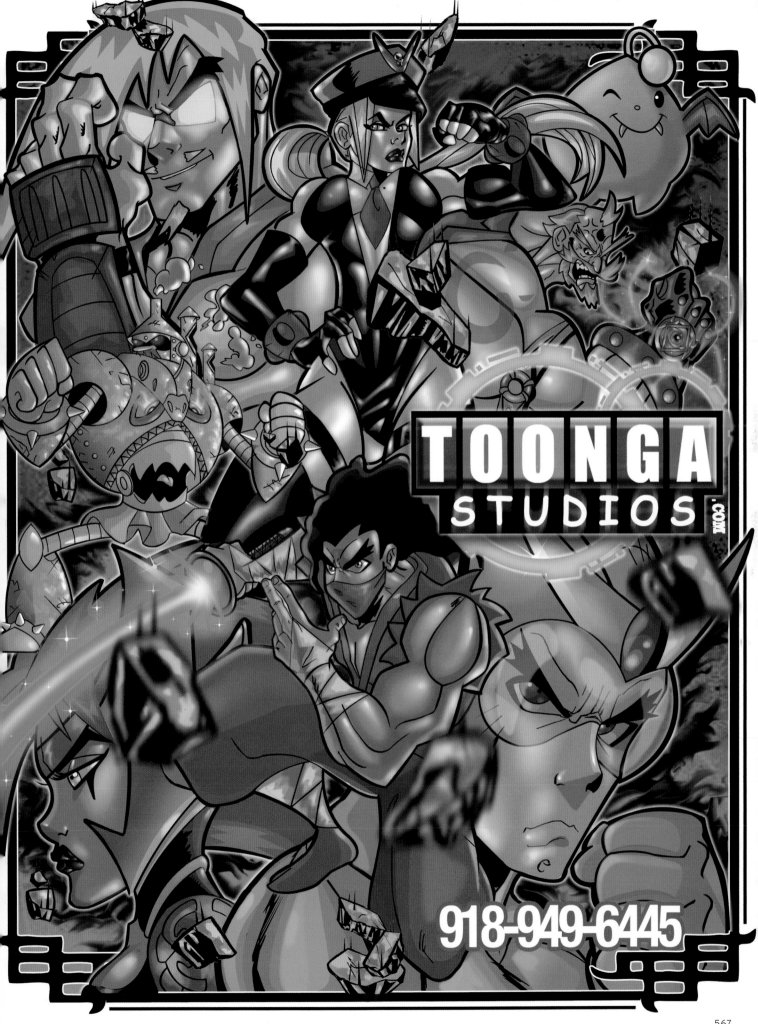

TOONGA STUDIOS.com

918-949-6445

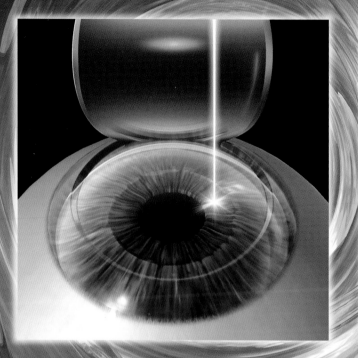
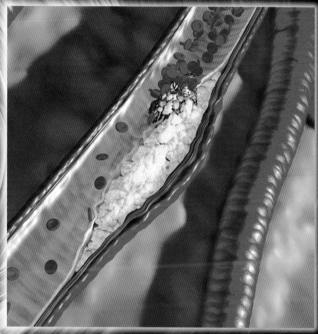

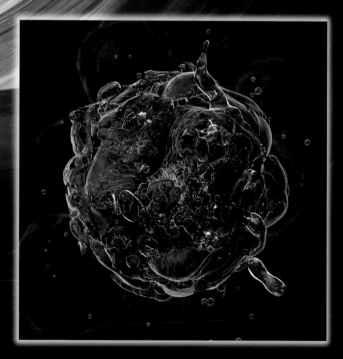

William Rieser
415 389 0332   •   R2design.com

IN BERNIE WE TRUST

Super realistic digital illustration in photographic or brush painted styles for advertising and packaging.
Specialising in Figurative, Chocolate, Fruit, Food, Drink, Landscapes and Seascapes.
Tel; +44 (0)1205 761793 Email; vincentwakerley@btinternet.com Webfolio; www.vincentwakerley.com

VICTOR LENUZZA

Julie Maren   303.641.6764   juliemaren.com

KIRK
WARREN
STUDIO

::
204.295.6248
::
kirkwarrenstudio.com
::
kirkwarren@shaw.ca

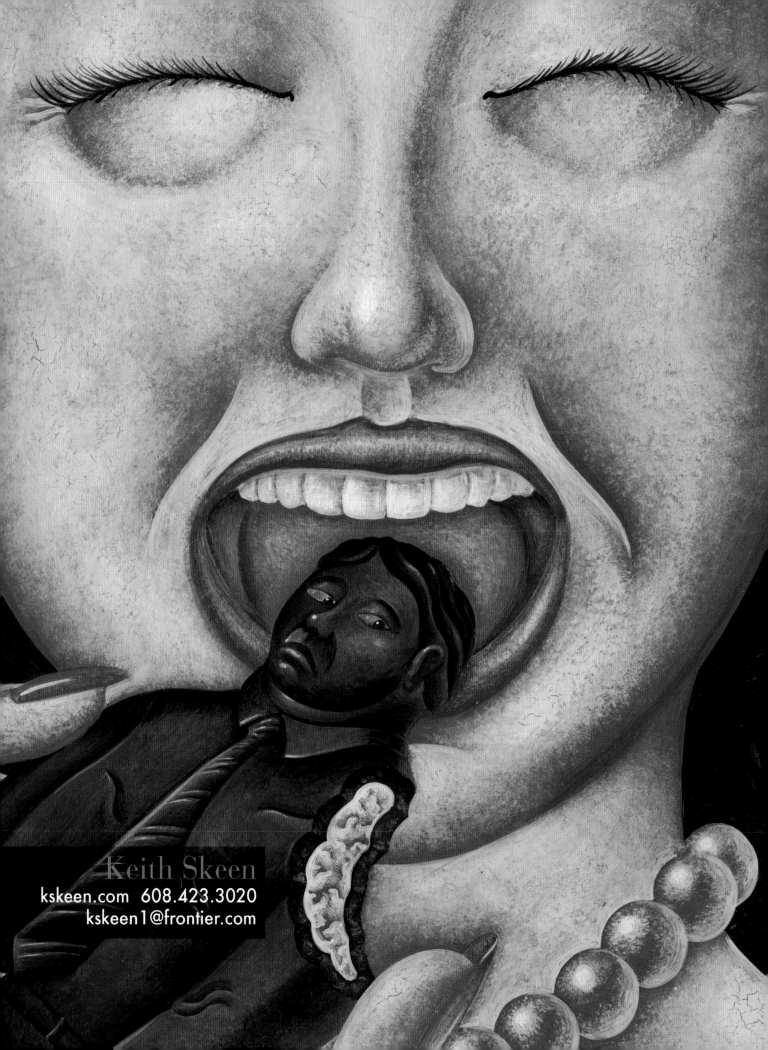

JERIANNE VAN DIJK

ILLUSTRATION/DESIGN

530-271-7128
Jerianneillustration.com

jan.murphy@mac.com | 650.207.8395 | murphyartworks.com

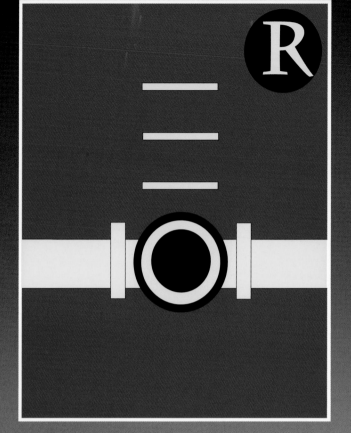
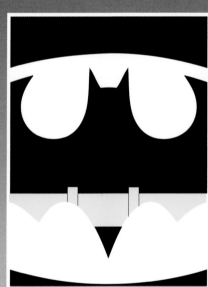

chriskotsakis

856.829.4065   chris@chriskotsakis.com   chriskotsakis.com

Michael Ortiz • Illustrator
(415) 819.5692 • michaeleortiz@gmail.com
www.michaeleortiz.com

MARCIA KLIOZE

kliozem@yahoo.com 703.402.3327 www.kliozeart.com

Partial client list: *Washington Post - Washington Times - WallStreet Journal - National Institutes of Health*

Mai Ly Degnan Illustration

www.mailyillustration.com

mailyillustration@gmail.com (863) 224-8522

Humza Khan
Concept Designer & Illustrator
248-762-2303
humza-khan@hotmail.com

www.humzakhan.com

TONI&GUY - Identity brand crest
Client: JDO. UK

FOX BARREL

Fox Barrel Cider - Brand icon
Lettering: Chris Weir
www.brandlettering.co.uk
Client: Tuffield. UK

Sacred Gin - Brand identity
Lettering by Chris Weir. www.brandlettering.co.uk
Client: Elmwood. UK

Absolut Vodka - Character brand icon
Client: The Brand Union. Sweden

Carling Beer - Brand crest icon
Client: Echo Brand Design. UK

Serengeti Beer - Leopard brand icon
Client: JKR. Jones Knowles Ritchie. UK

Bohemia Beer - Character brand icon
Client: Design Bridge. UK

Indio Beer - Brand icon
Client: Bulletproof. UK

epicicons
by
CHRIS MITCHELL
ILLUSTRATIVE GLOBAL BRANDS

T/F + 44 (0) 1243 572 099
M + 44 (0) 7802 874 349
E chris@epicicons.com
W www.epicicons.com

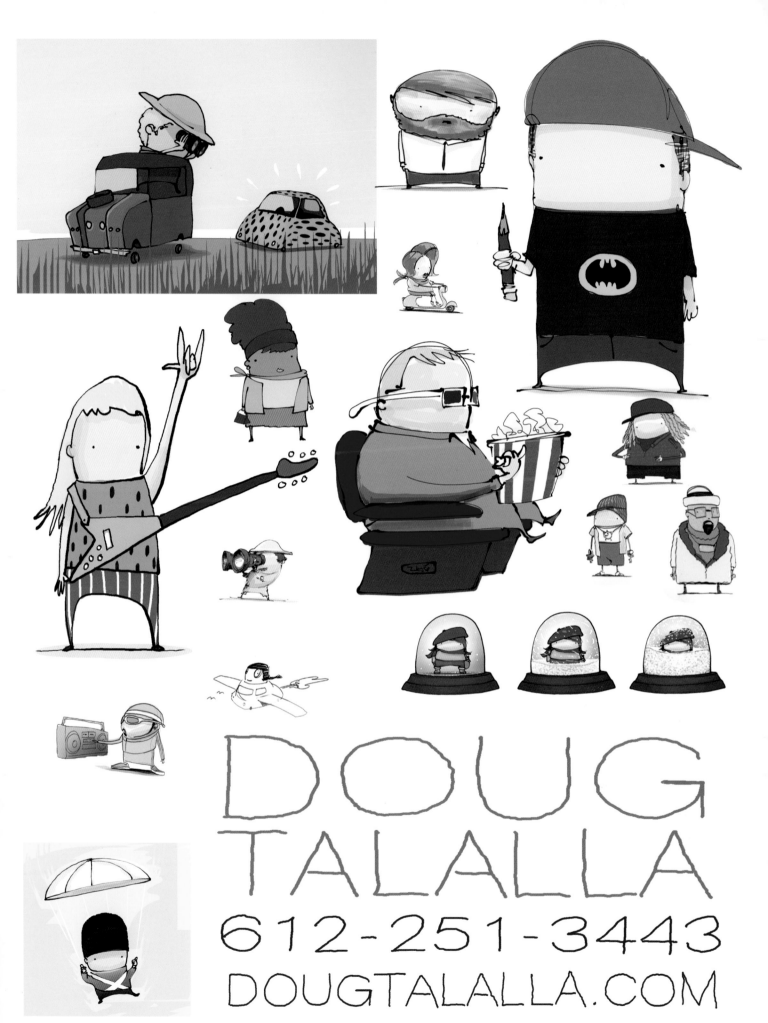

CHRISTOPHE VORLET

434·296·6502   christophe@vorlet.com

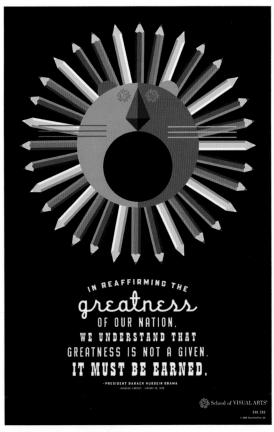

SCHOOL OF VISUAL ARTS

SCHOOL OF VISUAL ARTS

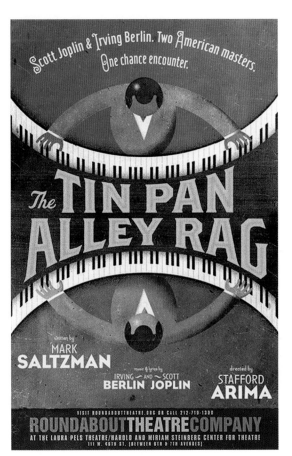

ROUNDABOUT THEATRE COMPANY

NIKE

☀ JON LAING STUDIOS

http://jonlaing.com • http://jonlaing.tumblr.com • info@jonlaing.com • 1 (732) 977-6472

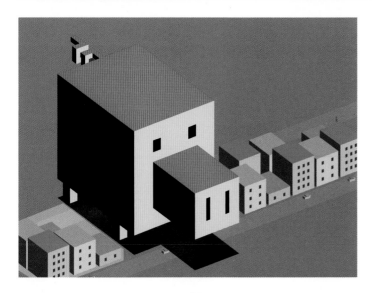

589

John Francis

jfrancis.com   303.595.3805   john@jfrancis.com

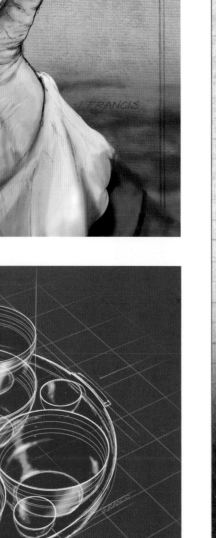

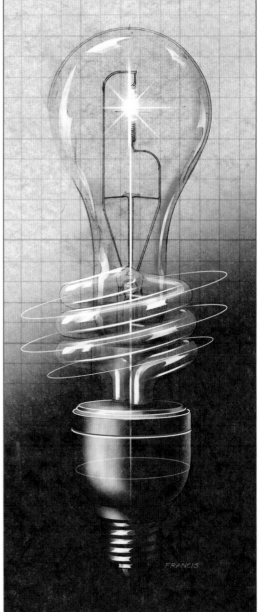

Kievan Havens

tel: 917-602-0915 | kgh.KievanHavens@gmail.com | www.KievanHavens.com

pulpstudios.ca/a.php

pulpstudios.ca/b.php   pulpstudios.ca/c.php   pulpstudios.ca/d.php   pulpstudios.ca/e.php   pulpstudios.ca/f.php

Scan QR Code and place smartphone over corresponding dotted lines...
TO BE AMAZED!

ILLUSTRATION I ANIMATION I MOTION GRAPHICS
CHARACTER DESIGN I ART DIRECTION

WWW.PULPSTUDIOS.CA
service@pulpstudios.ca

592

c + 212 996 2136
e + lynnefoster@mac.com
http://altpick.com/lynnfoster

lynnefoster
llustration ■ motion ■ multimedia

STEVEN NOBLE

SCRATCHBOARD   **LINE ART**   **ENGRAVINGS**   **WOODCUTS**

steve@stevennoble.com   direct: 707-789-0166   mobile: 415-897-6961   www.stevennoble.com

© 2012 Gatehouse Partners

© 2012 Fratelli Orsini

© 2012 John F. Kennedy

© 2012 William Sonoma

© 2012 "The Federalist"

© 2012 Jack Kemp

© 2012 Kraken Rum

© 2012 Rooster Farms

CHARDONNAY TRAIL

© 2012 Terlato Wines

© Copyright 2012 WHHA Logo

World Class Illustrations from over 3,500 images and over 1,000 stock illustrations for clients from all over the world!

2006 Rosey Awards • Mead Show Award Winner 2001 • Brand New 2009 • Ad Pulp 2009 • Communications Arts 1997 • National Addy Awards 2010

© 2012 William Sonoma

© 2012 Charging Bull

© Copyright 2012 Short Mountain Shine

© 2012 Dobel Tequila

© 2012 La Tortilla Factory

© 2012 Crossway Publishing

© Copyright 2012 Medjool Dates

© 2012 Rhubarb / William Sonoma

NAPA COUNTY CALIFORNIA

STATE OF IOWA

WE PRIZE AND · OUR RIGHTS
OUR LIBERTIES · WE WILL MAINTAIN

GENERAL ASSEMBLY

© Copyright 2011 State of Iowa "General Assembly"

© Angel's Share logo Identity

© 2012 Cracker Barrel

© Copyright 2011 William Sonoma

© 2012 Redwood Hill Farms

APPLIED UNDERWRITERS CAPTIVE RISK ASSURANCE CO

© 2011 Fetzer Vineyards

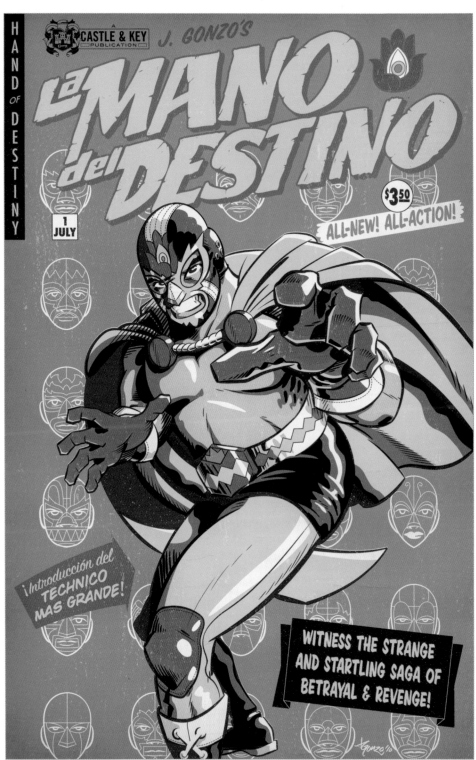

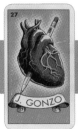

JASON GONZÁLEZ gonzo@jgonzodesigns.com • jgonzodesigns.com

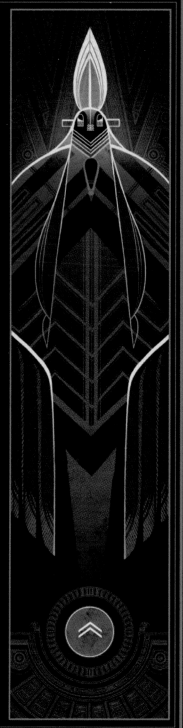

DENNY KHURNIAWAN

DESIGN / ILLUSTRATION / DIRECTION

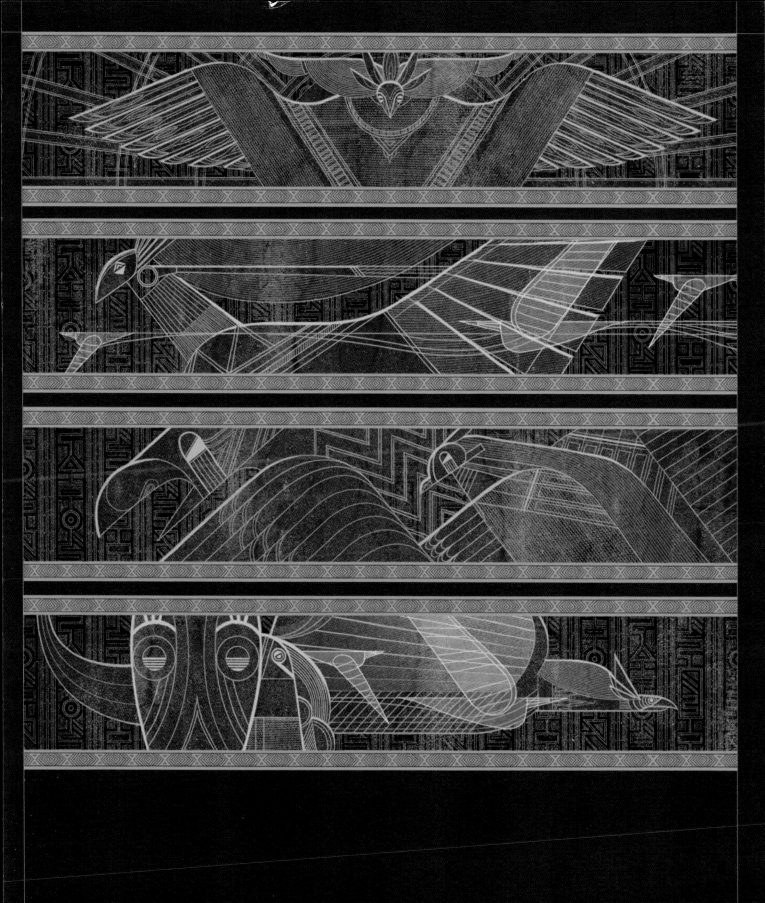

310 866 7113
mail@dkhurniawan.com
dkhurniawan.com

erika steiskal

erikasteiskal.com   erikasteiskal@gmail.com   330.718.1283

VERONICA LAWLOR   veronica@studio1482.com   212.570.5187 ext.10

GREG BETZA   greg@studio1482.com   212.570.5187 ext.12

Adventures
of
Huckleberry Finn

MARK TWAIN

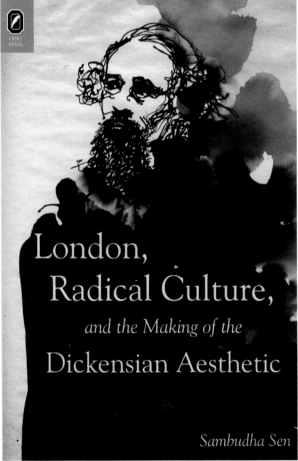

London,
Radical Culture,
and the Making of the
Dickensian Aesthetic

Sambudha Sen

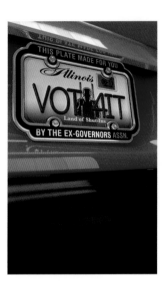

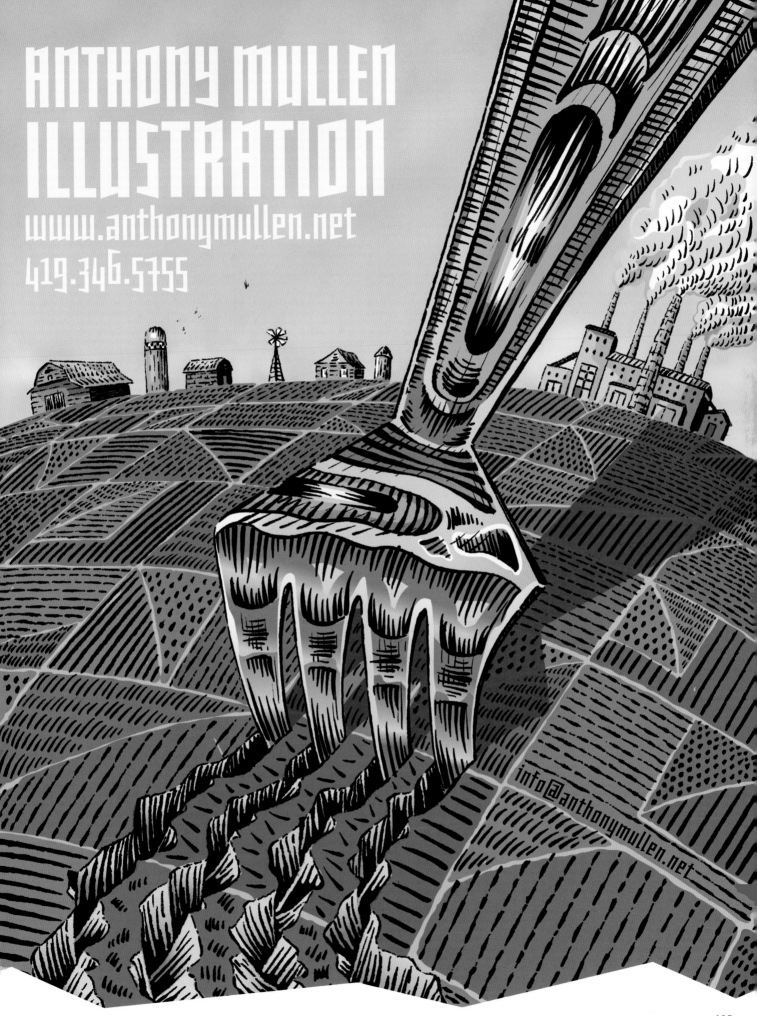

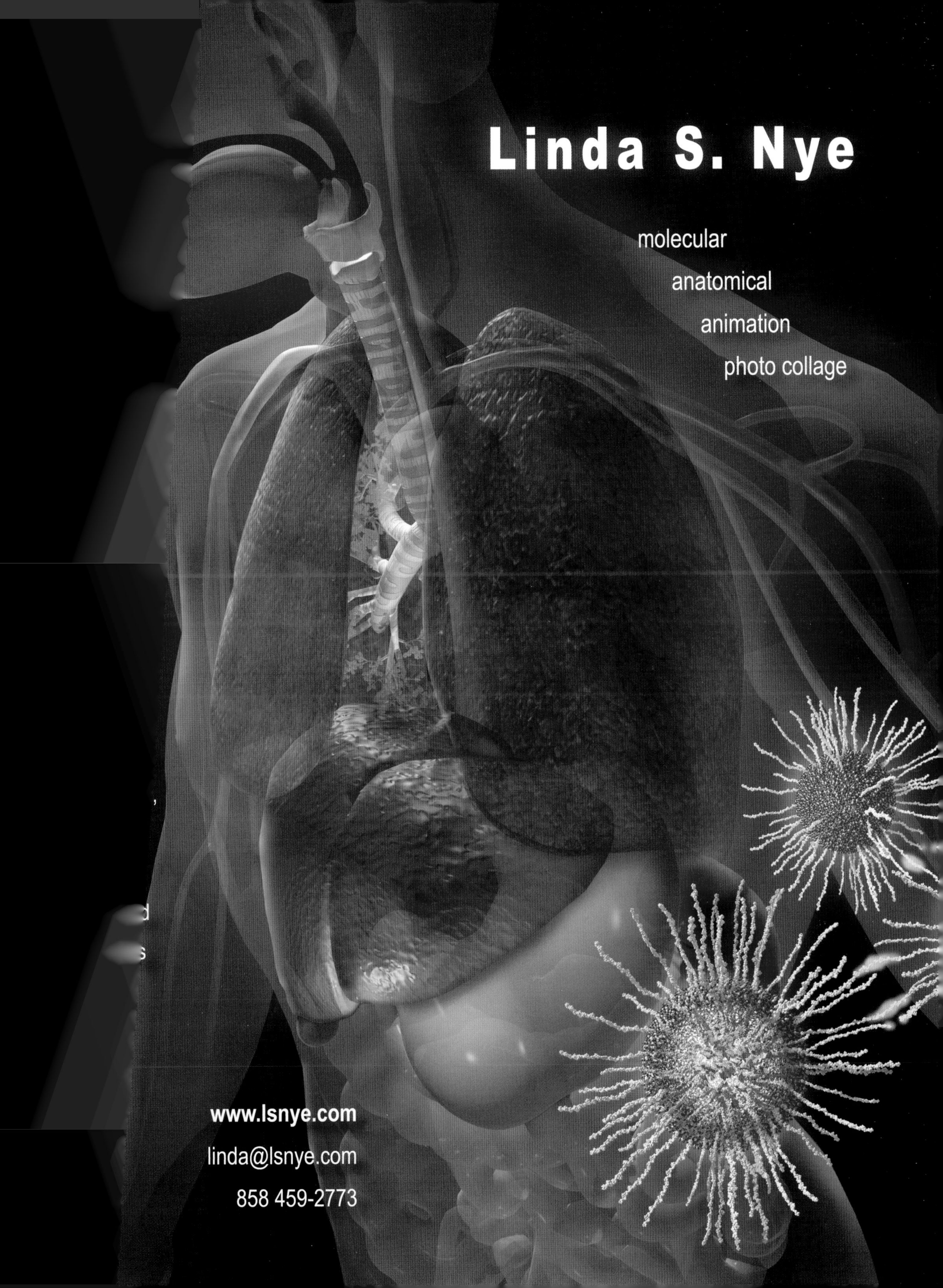

Linda S. Nye

molecular

anatomical

animation

photo collage

www.lsnye.com

linda@lsnye.com

858 459-2773

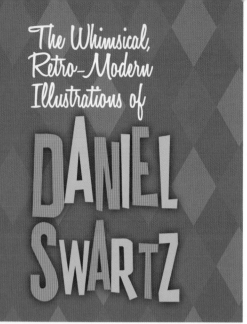

The Whimsical, Retro-Modern Illustrations of

DANIEL SWARTZ

The 'People' Person

Penny Weber
ILLUSTRATION

www.pennyweberart.com ~ (631) 419-0303
Represented by WendyLynn & Company ~ www.wendylynn.com

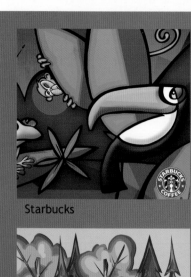

Starbucks

Minute Maid Park

Rebar Man

House of Cards

Point DeFiance Zoo

Seventeen

Dolphin Play Area

Opus Detectives

Todd Nordling Illustration-206.624.4996
toddnordling.com

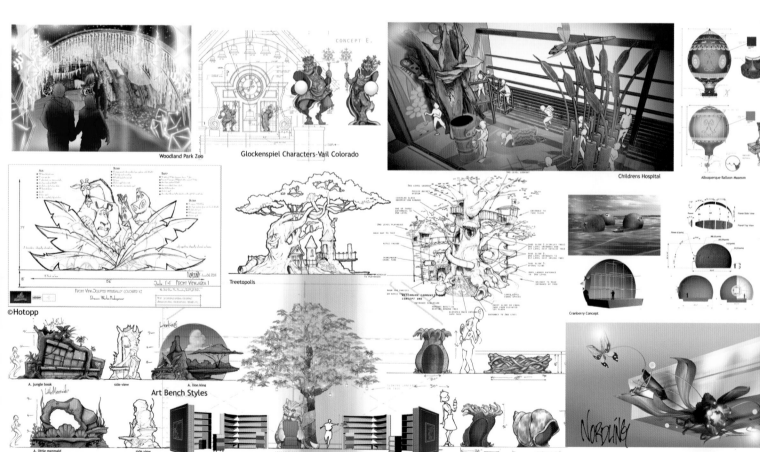

Woodland Park Zoo

Glockenspiel Characters-Vail Colorado

CONCEPT E.

Childrens Hospital

Albuquerque Balloon Museum

©Hotopp

Treetopolis

Cranberry Concept

A. Jungle book   side view   A. lion king

Art Bench Styles

A. little mermaid   side view

NORDLING

Todd Nordling Concept Design-206.624.4996
toddnordling.com

Robert L. Prince

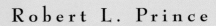

972-491-6779

robertlprince.com

BRIAN ALLEN
WWW.FLYLANDDESIGNS.COM
BRIAN@FLYLANDDESIGNS.COM
814.571.6141

www.MeganHalsey.com ✳ 215-834-3894 ✳ MHalseyArt@me.com

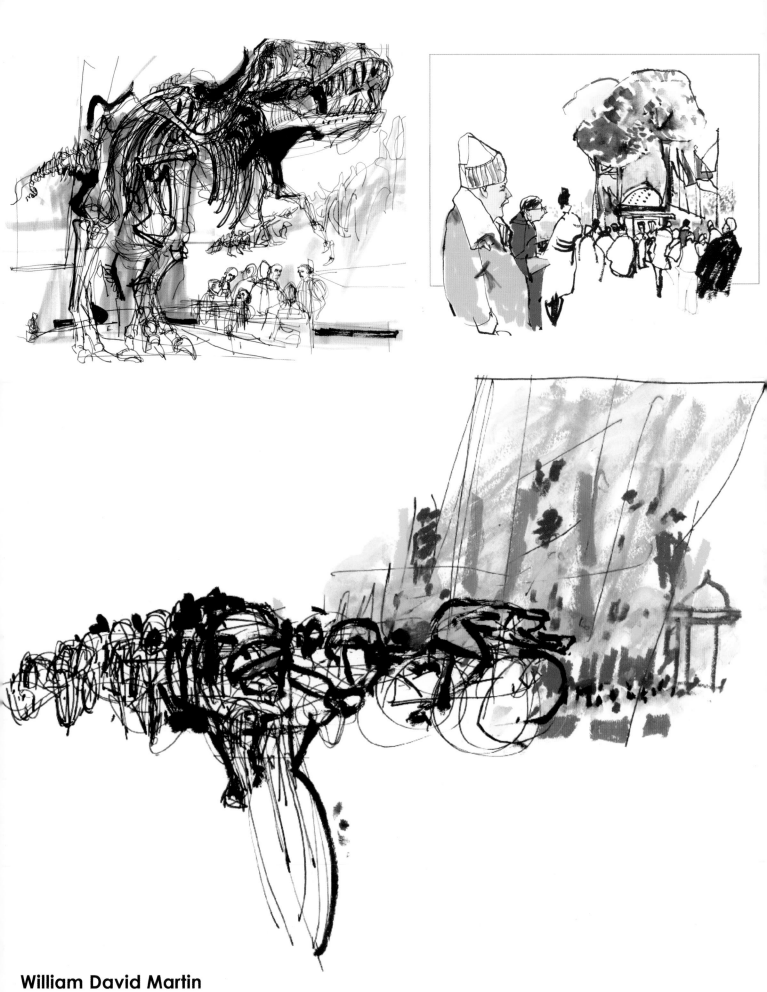

William David Martin

973-270-6603 • www.wdmdesigns.com

Science-Art.Com

Search — Find — Connect

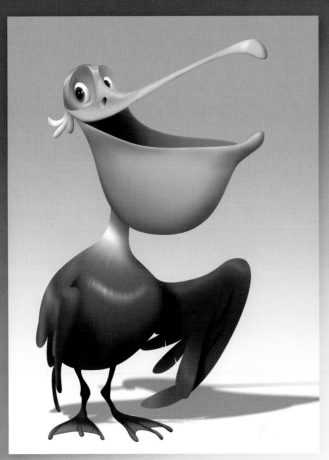

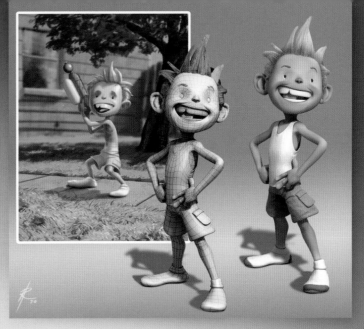

Rares Halmagean | www.rarebrush.com | 214.926.4575 | rares@rarebrush.com

JEFF SANSON

JSANSON@CMADESIGN.COM

(713) 834-0179

BANNER ILLUSTRATION

518.583.7982
sban28@hotmail.com
www.shawnbanner.com

Halsted Craig Hannah

415-823-0843

www.hchannah.com

Contagion. Director: Steven Soderbergh, Warner Bros. Pictures

PÍCA
(pē-käh)

"TALK TO THE CLAW"

STEVE PICA

stevepica.com/portfolio   727.686.6363   art@stevepica.com

Karol Kaminski

330-225-8195
karoldraws@roadrunner.com
www.karolkaminski.com

CHANGE MAKERS

RYAN ETTER ryanetterillustration.com **816.373.0586** info@ryanetterillustration.com

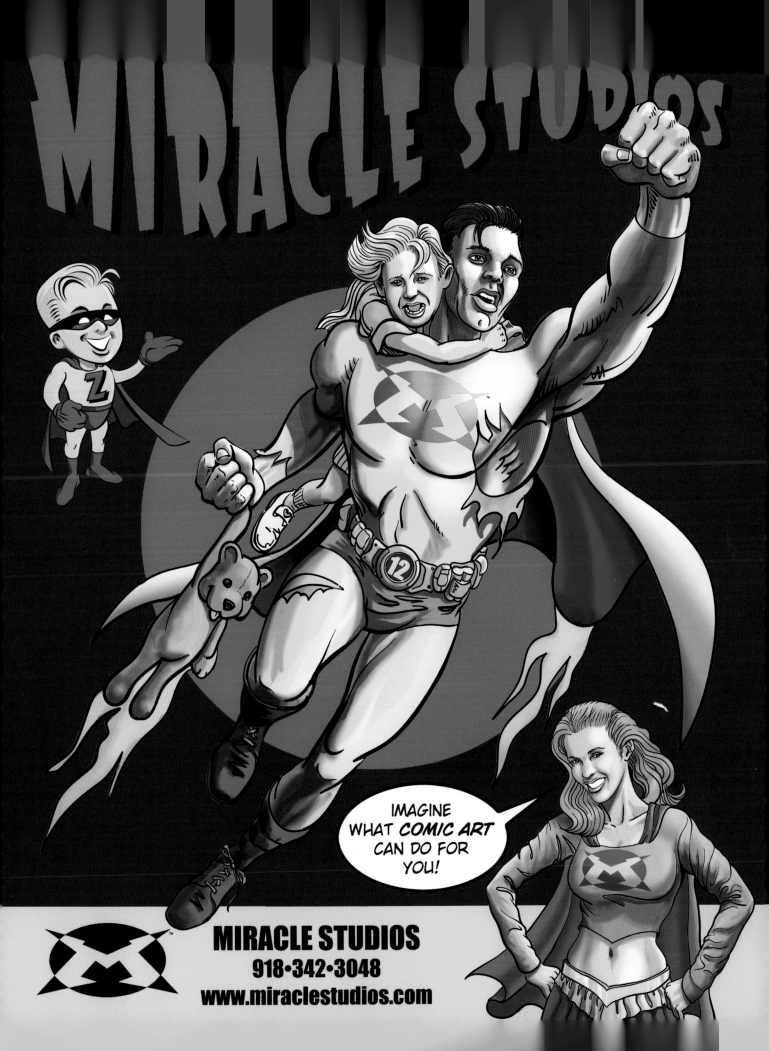

Richard Bornemann
3D Illustration and Animation
www.bccreative.com
978-266-0136   txt: 781-775-1866
rbornemann@verizon.net

Selected clients:
Cisco
Costco
Skyworks
Mont Blanc
Analogic
Kaspersky
Maidenform
Wired Magazine
Weight Watchers
Spike DDB
Hypertronics
BrightSource Solar
L3 Communications
Tyco
Rapiscan
Copley Controls
Passport Systems
Sensitech
Morgan Solar
Harvest Power
Reveal
DSA Detection Systems

Richard Bornemann   www.bccreative.com   rbornemann@verizon.net   978-266-0136   txt: 781-775-1866   Boston MA

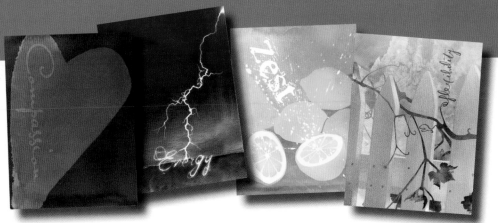

smart.

karen greenberg
illustration+
646.894.5796
karengreenberg.com

631

DIRECTORY

OF

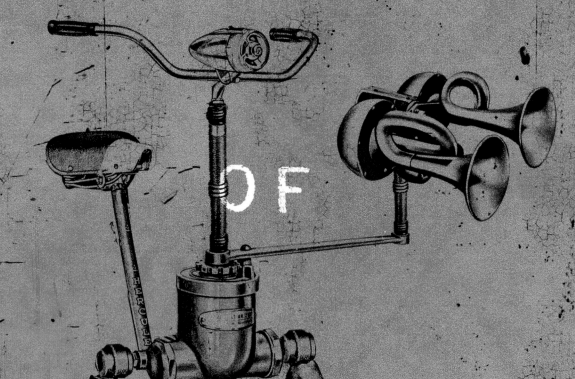

ILLUSTRATION

NO. 29

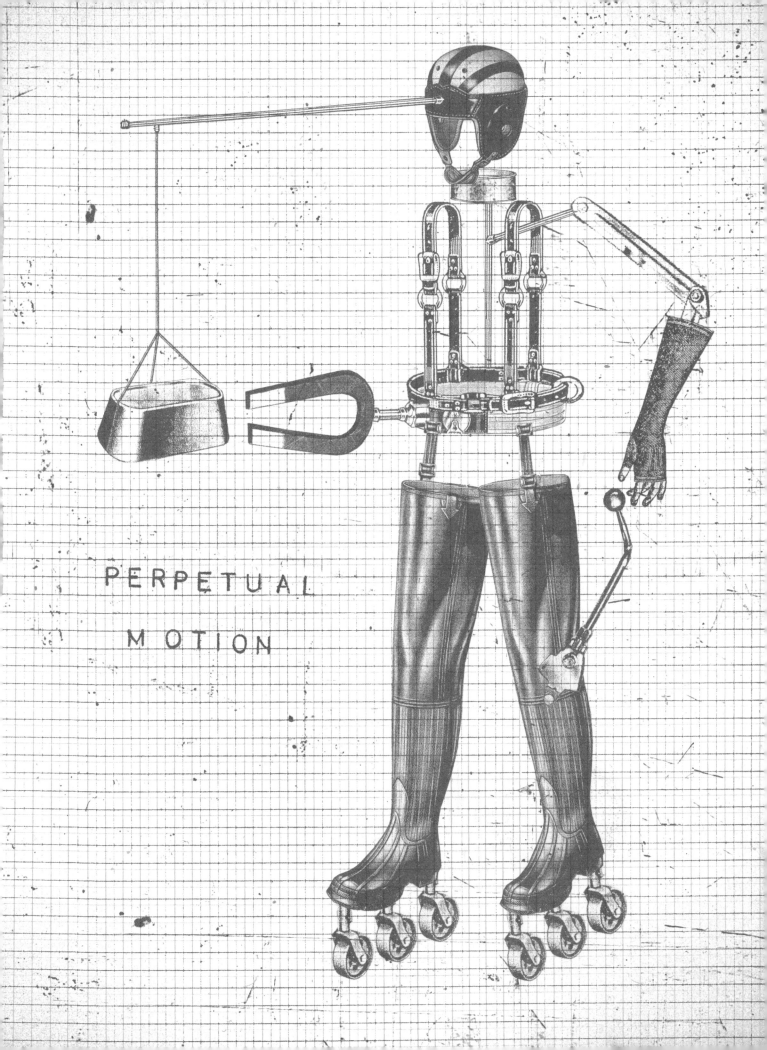

PERPETUAL

MOTION

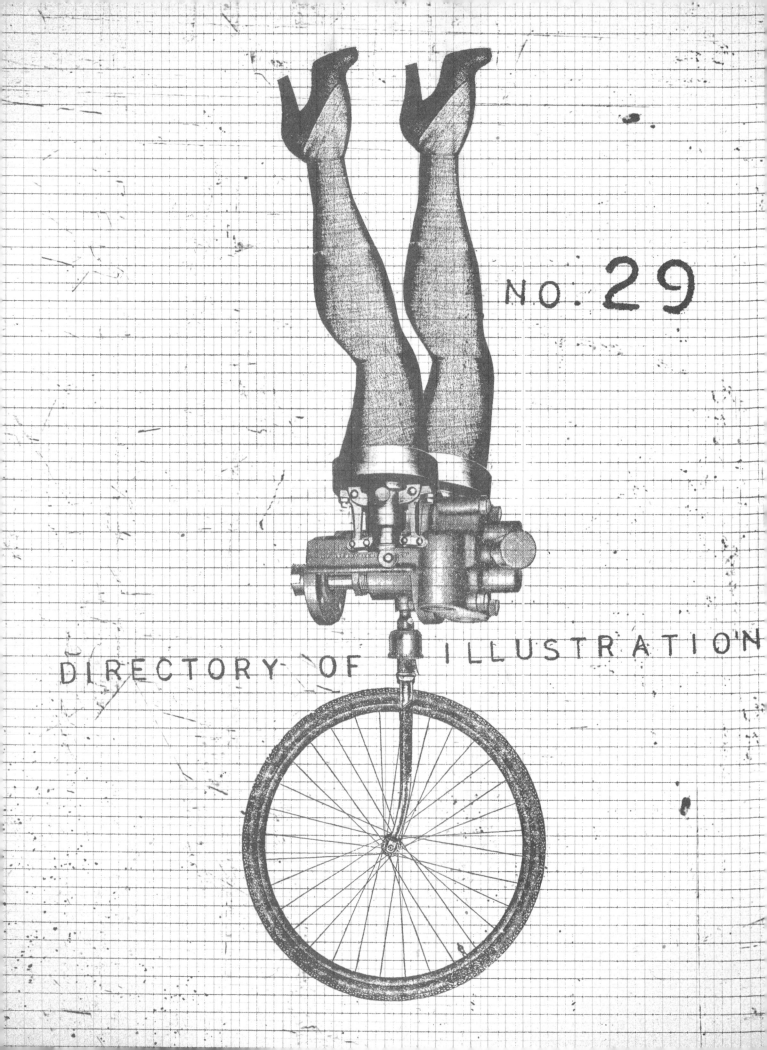

NO. 29

DIRECTORY OF ILLUSTRATION